SKILLS · FOR ·

Radiotelephony

CAO Procedures — VFR RT Communications — UK Procedures

7

Oxford
aviation academy

This book has been produced by Oxford Aviation Academy.

Production Team

Subject Specialists
Tony Pearson, Trevor Denning, Les Fellows

Created and Compiled by:
James Kenny

Editors:
Rick Harland, Lesley Smith

Cover Design by: Chris Hill

Cover Photograph by: BAA Aviation Ltd.

First Published by: Oxford Aviation Academy, Oxford, England, 2007

Printed in Singapore by: KHL Printing Co. Pte Ltd

Contact Details:
OAAmedia
Oxford Aviation Academy
Oxford Airport
Kidlington
Oxford
OX5 1QX
England

Tel: +44 (0)1865 844290

Email: **info@oaamedia.com**

Innovative learning solutions for

www.oaamedia.com   ISBN 978-0-9555177-6-1   www.oaa.com

TABLE OF CONTENTS

RADIO TELEPHONY COMMUNICATIONS

FOREWORD	v
TO THE PILOT	xiii
CHAPTER 1: VHF VOICE COMMUNICATIONS	1
CHAPTER 2: GENERAL OPERATING PROCEDURES	11
CHAPTER 3: GENERAL PHRASEOLOGY	35
CHAPTER 4: AERODROME CONTROL	47
CHAPTER 5: APPROACH CONTROL	71
CHAPTER 6: THE FLIGHT INFORMATION SERVICE	81
CHAPTER 7: GENERAL RADAR PHRASEOLOGY	91
CHAPTER 8: COMMUNICATION FAILURE	107
CHAPTER 9: DISTRESS AND URGENCY	115
CHAPTER 10: VHF PROPAGATION	123
CHAPTER 11: WEATHER INFORMATION	131
CHAPTER 12: VFR FLIGHT SCENARIO	141
CHAPTER 13: UNITED KINGDOM RT DIFFERENCES	159
CHAPTER 14: VFR FLIGHT SCENARIO IN THE UNITED KINGDOM	199
CHAPTER 15: QUESTIONS AND ANSWERS	215
RADIOTELEPHONY COMMUNICATIONS SYLLABUS	233
INDEX	235

FOREWORD TO THE SECOND EDITION.

INTRODUCTION.

Whether you are planning to fly microlights, space shuttles, gliders, combat aircraft, airliners or light aircraft, it is essential that you have a firm grasp of the theoretical knowledge which underpins practical piloting skills. This Oxford Aviation Academy "Skills for Flight" series of text books covers the fundamental theory with which all pilots must come to grips from the very beginning of their pilot training, and which must remain with them throughout their flying career, if they are to be masters of the art and science of flight.

JOINT AVIATION AUTHORITIES PILOTS' LICENCES.

Joint Aviation Authorities (JAA) pilot licences were first introduced in Europe in 1999. By 2006, almost every JAA member state, including all the major countries of Europe, had adopted this new, pan-European licensing system at Air Transport Pilot's Licence, Commercial Pilot's Licence and Private Pilot's Licence levels, and many other countries, world-wide, had expressed interest in aligning their training with the JAA pilot training syllabi.

These syllabi, and the regulations governing the award and the renewal of licences, are defined by the JAA's licensing agency, 'Joint Aviation Requirements - Flight Crew Licensing', (JAR-FCL). JAR-FCL training syllabi are published in a document known as 'JAR-FCL 1.'

The United Kingdom Civil Aviation Authority (UK CAA) is one of the founder authorities within the JAA. The UK CAA has been administering examinations and skills tests for the issue of JAA licences since the year 2000, on behalf of JAR-FCL.

The Private Pilot's Licence (PPL), then, issued by the UK CAA, is a JAA licence which is accepted as proof of a pilot's qualifications throughout all JAA member states.

Currently, the JAA member states are: *United Kingdom, Denmark, Iceland, Switzerland, France, Sweden, Netherlands, Belgium, Romania, Spain, Finland, Ireland, Malta, Norway, Czech Republic, Slovenia, Germany, Portugal, Greece, Italy, Turkey, Croatia, Poland, Austria, Estonia, Lithuania, Cyprus, Hungary, Luxembourg, Monaco, Slovakia.*

As a licence which is also fully compliant with the licensing recommendations of the International Civil Aviation Organisation (ICAO), the JAA PPL is also valid in most other parts of the world.

The JAA PPL in the UK has replaced the full UK PPL, formerly issued solely under the authority of the UK CAA.

Issue of the JAA PPL is dependent on the student pilot having completed the requisite training and passed the appropriate theoretical knowledge and practical flying skills tests detailed in 'JAR-FCL 1'. In the UK, the CAA is responsible for ensuring that these requirements are met before any licence is issued.

EUROPEAN AVIATION SAFETY AGENCY.

With the establishment of the European Aviation Safety Agency (EASA), it is envisaged that JAA flight crew licensing and examining competency will be absorbed into the EASA organisation. It is possible that, when this change has taken place, the PPL may even change its title again, with the words "EASA" replacing "JAA". However, we do not yet know this for certain. In the UK, such a step would require the British Government to review and, where necessary, revise the Civil Aviation Act. But, whatever the future of the title of the PPL, the JAA pilot's licence syllabi are unlikely to change fundamentally, in the short term. So, for the moment, the JAA Licence remains, and any change in nomenclature is likely to be just that: a change in name only.

OXFORD AVIATION ACADEMY AND OAAMEDIA.

Oxford Aviation Academy (OAA) is one of the world's leading professional pilot schools. It has been in operation for over forty years and has trained more than 15 000 professional pilots for over 80 airlines, world-wide.

OAA was the first pilot school in the United Kingdom to be granted approval to train for the JAA ATPL. OAA led and coordinated the joint-European effort to produce the JAR-FCL ATPL Learning Objectives which are now published by the JAA, itself, as a guide to the theoretical knowledge requirements of ATPL training.

OAA's experience in European licensing, at all levels, and in the use of advanced training technologies, led OAA's training material production unit, OAAmedia, to conceive, create and produce multimedia, computer-based training for ATPL students preparing for JAA theoretical knowledge examinations by distance learning. Subsequently, OAAmedia extended its range of computer-based training CD-ROMs to cover PPL and post-PPL studies.

This present series of text books is designed to complement OAAmedia's successful PPL CD-ROMs in helping student pilots prepare for the theoretical knowledge examinations of the JAA PPL and beyond, as well as to provide students with the aviation knowledge they require to become safe and competent pilots.

The OAA expertise embodied in this series of books means that students working towards the JAA PPL have access to top-quality, up-to-date, study material at an affordable cost. Those students who aspire to becoming professional pilots will find that this series of PPL books takes them some way beyond PPL towards the knowledge required for professional pilot licences.

THE JAA PRIVATE PILOT'S LICENCE (AEROPLANES).

The following information on the Joint Aviation Authorities Private Pilot's Licence (Aeroplanes); (JAA PPL(A)) is for your guidance only. Full details of flying training, theoretical knowledge training and the corresponding tests and examinations are contained in the JAA document: **JAR–FCL 1, SUBPART C – PRIVATE PILOT LICENCE (Aeroplanes) – PPL(A).**

The privileges of the JAA PPL (A) allow you to fly as pilot-in-command, or co-pilot, of any aircraft for which an appropriate rating is held, but not for remuneration, or on revenue-earning flights.

For United Kingdom based students, full details of JAA PPL (A) training and examinations can be found in the CAA publication, **Licensing Administration Standards Operating Requirements Safety (LASORS),** copies of which can be accessed through the CAA's Flight Crew Licensing website.

Flying Training.

The JAA PPL (A) can be gained by completing a course of a minimum of 45 hours flying training with a training organisation registered with the appropriate National Aviation Authority (the Civil Aviation Authority, in the case of the United Kingdom).

Flying instruction must normally include:

- 25 hours dual Instruction on aeroplanes.

- 10 hours supervised solo flight time on aeroplanes, which must include **5** hours solo cross-country flight time, including one cross-country flight of at least 150 nautical miles (270km), during which full-stop landings at two different aerodromes, different from the aerodrome of departure, are to be made.

The required flying-instructional time may be reduced by a maximum of 10 hours for those students with appropriate flying experience on other types of aircraft.

The flying test (Skills Test), comprising navigation and general skills tests, is to be taken within 6 months of completing flying instruction. All sections of the Skills Test must be taken within a period of 6 months. A successfully completed Skills Test has a period of validity of 12 months for the purposes of licence issue.

Theoretical Knowledge Examinations.

The procedures for the conduct of the JAA PPL (A) theoretical knowledge examinations will be determined by the National Aviation Authority of the state concerned, (the Civil Aviation Authority, in the case of the United Kingdom).

The JAA theoretical knowledge examination must comprise the following 9 subjects: *Air Law, Aircraft General Knowledge, Flight Performance and Planning, Human Performance and Limitations, Meteorology, Navigation, Operational Procedures, Principles of Flight, Communication.*

A single examination paper may cover several subjects.

The combination of subjects and the examination paper titles, as administered by the UK CAA, are, at present:

1. Air Law and Operational Procedures.
2. Human Performance and Limitations.
3. Navigation & Radio Aids.
4. Meteorology.
5. Aircraft (General) & Principles of Flight.
6. Flight Performance and Planning.
7. JAR-FCL Communications (PPL) (i.e. Radiotelephony Communications).

The majority of the questions are multiple choice. In the United Kingdom, examinations are normally conducted by the Flying Training Organisation or Registered Facility at which a student pilot carries out his training.

The pass mark in all subjects is 75%.

For the purpose of the issue of a JAA PPL(A), a pass in the theoretical knowledge examinations will be accepted during the 24 month period immediately following the date of successfully completing all of the theoretical knowledge examinations.

Medical Requirements.
An applicant for a JAR-FCL PPL(A) must hold a valid JAR-FCL Class 1 or Class 2 Medical Certificate.

THE UNITED KINGDOM NATIONAL PRIVATE PILOT'S LICENCE (AEROPLANES).

One of the aims of the United Kingdom National Private Pilot's Licence (UK NPPL) is to make it easier for the recreational flyer to obtain a PPL than it would be if the requirements of the standard JAA-PPL had to be met. The regulations governing medical fitness are also different between the UK NPPL and the JAA PPL.

Full details of the regulations governing the training for, issue of, and privileges of the UK NPPL may be found by consulting LASORS and the Air Navigation Order. Most UK flying club websites also give details of this licence.

Basically, the holder of a UK NPPL is restricted to flight in a simple, UK-registered, single piston-engine aeroplane (including motor gliders and microlights) whose Maximum Authorized Take-off Weight does not exceed 2000 kg. Flight is normally permitted in UK airspace only, by day, and in accordance with the Visual Flight Rules.

Flying Training.
Currently, 32 hours of flying training is required for the issue of a UK NPPL (A), of which 22 hours are to be dual instruction, and 10 hours to be supervised solo flying time.

There are separate general and navigation skills tests.

Theoretical Knowledge Examinations.
The UK NPPL theoretical knowledge syllabus and ground examinations are the same as for the JAA PPL (A). This series of books, therefore, is also suitable for student pilots preparing for the UK NPPL.

THE UNITED KINGDOM FLIGHT RADIOTELEPHONY OPERATOR'S LICENCE.

Although there is a written paper on Radiotelephony Communications in the JAA PPL theoretical knowledge examinations, pilots in the United Kingdom, and in most other countries, who wish to operate airborne radio equipment will need to take a separate practical test for the award of a Flight Radiotelephony Operators Licence (FRTOL). For United Kingdom based students, full details of the FRTOL are contained in LASORS.

NOTES ON CONTENT AND TEXT.

Technical Content.

The technical content of this OAA series of pilot training text books aims to reach the standard required by the theoretical knowledge syllabus of the JAA Private Pilot's Licence (Aeroplanes), (JAA PPL(A)). This is the minimum standard that has been aimed at. The subject content of several of the volumes in the series exceeds PPL standard. However, all questions and their answers, as well as the margin notes, are aimed specifically at the JAA PPL (A) ground examinations.

An indication of the technical level covered by each text book is given in individual subject prefaces. The books deal predominantly with single piston-engine aeroplane operations.

Questions and Answers.

Questions appear at the end of this book, in order that readers may test themselves on the main subject(s) covered by the book. The questions are of the same format as the questions asked in the JAA PPL (A) theoretical knowledge examinations, as administered by the UK CAA. All questions are multiple-choice, containing four answer options, one of which is the correct answer, with the remaining three options being incorrect "distracters".

Students Working for a Non-JAA PPL.

JAA licence training syllabi follow the basic structure of ICAO-recommended training, so even if the national PPL you are working towards is not issued by a JAA member state, this series of text books should provide virtually all the training material you need. Theoretical knowledge examinations for the JAA PPL are, however, administered nationally, so there will always be country-specific aspects to JAA PPL examinations. 'Air Law' is the most obvious subject where country-specific content is likely to remain; the other subject is 'Navigation', where charts will most probably depict the terrain of the country concerned.

As mentioned elsewhere in this Foreword, this series of books is also suitable for student pilots preparing for the United Kingdom National Private Pilot's Licence (UK NPPL). The theoretical examination syllabus and examinations for the UK NPPL are currently identical to those for the JAA PPL.

Student Helicopter Pilots.

Of the seven book in this series, the following are suitable for student helicopters pilots working towards the JAA PPL (H), the UK NPPL (H) or the equivalent national licence:

Volume 1: 'Air Law & Operational Procedures'; Volume 2: 'Human Performance'; Volume 3: 'Navigation & Radio Aids'; Volume 4: 'Meteorology', and Volume 7: 'Radiotelephony'.

The OAAmedia Website.

If any errors of content are identified in these books, or if there are any JAA PPL (A) theoretical knowledge syllabus changes, Oxford Aviation Academy's aim is to record those changes on the product support pages of the OAAmedia website, at: www.oaamedia.com

Grammatical Note.

It is standard grammatical convention in the English language, as well as in most other languages of Indo-European origin, that a single person of unspecified gender should be referred to by the appropriate form of the masculine singular pronoun, *he*, *him*, or *his*. This convention has been used throughout this series of books in order to avoid the pitfalls of usage that have crept into some modern works which contain frequent and distracting repetitions of *he or she*, *him or her*, *etc*, or where the ungrammatical use of *they*, and related pronouns, is resorted to. In accordance with the teachings of English grammar, the use, in this series of books, of a masculine pronoun to refer to a single person of unspecified gender does not imply that the person is of the male sex.

Margin Notes.

You will notice that margin notes appear on some pages in these books, identified by one of two icons:

a key 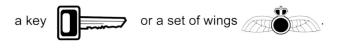 or a set of wings .

The key icon identifies a note which the authors judge to be a key point in the understanding of a subject; the wings identify what the authors judge to be a point of airmanship.

The UK Theoretical Knowledge Examination Papers.

The UK CAA sets examination papers to test JAA PPL (A) theoretical knowledge either as single-subject papers or as papers in which two subjects are combined.

Two examination papers currently cover two subjects each:

- **Aircraft (General) & Principles of Flight**: The 'Aircraft (General) & Principles of Flight' examination paper, as its title suggests, covers 'Principles of Flight' and those subjects which deal with the aeroplane as a machine, 'Airframes', 'Engines', 'Propellers' and 'Instrumentation', which JAR-FCL groups under the title 'Aircraft General Knowledge'.

- **Flight Performance & Planning:** The examination paper entitled 'Flight Performance & Planning' covers both 'Aeroplane Performance, and 'Mass & Balance'.

When preparing for the two examinations named above, using this Oxford series of text books, you will need **Volume 5, 'Principles of Flight'**, which includes 'Aeroplane Performance', and **Volume 6, 'Aeroplanes'**, which includes 'Mass & Balance' as well as 'Airframes', 'Engines', 'Propellers', and 'Instrumentation'. So to prepare for the 'Aircraft (General) & Principles of Flight' examination, you need to take the **'Aeroplanes'** infomation from **Volume 6** and the **'Principles of Flight'** information from **Volume 5**. When you are preparing for the 'Flight Performance & Planning' examination you need to take the **'Aeroplane Performance'** information from **Volume 5** and the **'Mass & Balance'** information from **Volume 6**.

It has been necessary to arrange the books in this way for reasons of space and subject logic. The titles of the rest of the volumes in the series correspond with the titles of the examinations. The situation is summed up for you in the table on the following page:

JAA Theoretical Examination Papers	Corresponding Oxford Book Title
Air Law and Operational Procedures	Volume 1: Air Law
Human Performance and Limitations	Volume 2: Human Performance
Navigation and Radio Aids	Volume 3: Navigation
Meteorology	Volume 4: Meteorology
Aircraft (General) and Principles of Flight	Volume 5: Principles of Flight Volume 6: Aeroplanes
Flight Performance and Planning	Volume 5: Aeroplane Performance Volume 6: Mass and Balance
JAR-FCL Communications (PPL)	Volume 7: Radiotelephony

Regulatory Changes.

Finally, so that you may stay abreast of any changes in the flying and ground training requirements pertaining to pilot licences which may be introduced by your national aviation authority, be sure to consult, from time to time, the relevant publications issued by the authority. In the United Kingdom, the Civil Aviation Publication, LASORS, is worth looking at regularly. It is currently accessible, on-line, on the CAA website at **www.caa.co.uk**.

Oxford,
England

June 2010

TO THE PILOT.

Radiotelephony (RT) is essential for the safe operation of aircraft wherever they fly.

Use of the RT enables a pilot to communicate with Air Traffic Service Units in order to obtain all kinds of information and instructions relating to the safe and expeditious conduct of his flight. Yet many student pilots find the process of learning to speak over the RT more daunting than actually learning to fly the aircraft.

This book has been conceived and produced primarily in order to help students, to acquire the RT knowledge, skills and techniques they will need to communicate competently, concisely and effectively with Air Traffic Service Units, when flying in accordance with the Visual Flight Rules (VFR).

The skills taught by the book cover all ICAO standard procedures, as well as United Kingdom differences to those procedures.

The VFR RT phraseology and procedures covered in Chapters 1 to 12 of this book are those laid down in ICAO Annex 10, Volume 2, and the ICAO Manual of Radiotelephony, Document 9432-AN 925; these items of phraseology and procedure are those agreed internationally and which govern VFR RT practice around the world.

Chapters 13 and 14 cover differences in RT phraseology and procedure used when United Kingdom Air Traffic Service Units communicate with pilots in United Kingdom airspace. Footnotes throughout the book also refer to differences between ICAO RT practice and United Kingdom RT practice.

United Kingdom (UK) RT phraseology and procedures are laid down by the UK Civil Aviation Authority's Manual of Radiotelephony, CAP 413. CAP 413 may be purchased in book form, or accessed via the UK CAA's website.

United Kingdom-based Student Pilots.
If you are a United Kingdom-based student pilot, working towards a JAR-FCL/EASA Private Pilot's Licence (PPL) or a UK National PPL, and preparing for the theoretical knowledge examination in VFR RT Communications, you must learn the whole content of this book, and refer to the latest edition of CAP 413. The same content will also be good preparation for the written and practical tests for the UK Flight Radiotelephony Operator's Licence (UK FRTOL). The questions at the end of this book, are designed specifically to help United Kingdom-based pilots to prepare for the JAR-FCL/EASA PPL theoretical knowledge examination in VFR Communications and the UK FRTOL tests.

UK-based students working towards a Commercial Pilot's Licence or Airline Transport Pilot's Licence, and who are using the book to prepare for the JAR-FCL theoretical knowledge VFR Communications examination, should study Chapters 1-12 only. However, if they are taking the UK FRTOL test, they will need to study the whole book, as well as refer to the latest edition of CAP 413.

Student Pilots Based outside the United Kingdom.
If you are a student pilot based outside the United Kingdom and preparing for a theoretical knowledge examination in VFR Communications, you should learn and apply the content of Chapters 1 to 12, only. Do, however, consult your national

aviation authority's examination syllabus before beginning your exam preparations.

Be aware that if you are preparing to sit a test for a Flight Radiotelephony Operator's Licence set by a national authority, you must be familiar with the national differences published by your country's civil aviation authority, in addition to standard ICAO RT procedures. RT Handbooks produced by national aviation authorities are the best guide to the differences between national and ICAO procedures.

CHAPTER 1
VHF VOICE COMMUNICATIONS

RADIOTELEPHONY COMMUNICATIONS.

Radiotelephony communications between aircraft and ground stations have been a feature of military and commercial aviation since the very early days of flying. But for the greater part of the 20th Century, radio was considered a luxury by pilots of light aircraft flying in accordance with Visual Flight Rules (VFR). However, from the 1970s, radios operating in the Very High Frequency (VHF) voice communication range rapidly became a standard fit in most light aircraft and, thereafter, aerodromes and airfields began to insist that aircraft operating from them, should be radio equipped.

Nowadays, the use of radio between aircraft and ground stations is absolutely essential for the safe operation of both commercial and light aircraft in air traffic environments which are growing ever busier. The name given to the use of radio in this way is "Radiotelephony". In popular, every-day parlance the word "Radiotelephony" is often abbreviated to RTF, or, more simply, RT. The abbreviation RTF is mostly used by national aviation authorities, and is the abbreviation you will often find in examinations.

RT is the abbreviation most commonly used by pilots. RT communications enable the pilot to obtain information and instructions for the safe conduct of his flight.

Consequently, today's aviators need to be skilled radio operators as well as pilots and navigators. It is the aim of this book to help you learn the RT skills you will need to fly in accordance with Visual Flight Rules anywhere in the world.

VHF FREQUENCY ALLOCATION.

The frequencies allocated to VHF voice communications are those from 118 Megahertz to 136.975 Megahertz (MHz).

Other VHF frequencies are allocated to certain pilot-interpreted radio-navigation and approach aids. For instance, the VOR navigation system and the Instrument Landing System operate in the VHF range 108 MHz to 117.975 MHz. These frequencies are sometimes employed for the one-way transmission of aerodrome information from ground stations to aircraft.

There will also be radio-navigation equipment in most light aircraft operating in frequency bands other than VHF. For instance, Automatic Direction Finding (ADF) equipment operates in the Medium to Low frequency bands, while Distance Measuring Equipment (DME) and transponders, which both work on the secondary radar principle, operate in the Ultra High Frequency (UHF) band.

The voice communication range of VHF frequencies is 118 MHz to 136.975 MHz.

However, here, we will deal only with matters concerning VHF voice communications. Typically, the VHF voice communication radios are labelled COMM whilst the VHF radio-navigation sets bear the label NAV, as shown in *Figure 1.1, overleaf.*

VHF Voice Communication Frequencies - 25kHz Spacing.
The frequencies which can be selected on the VHF radios fitted to most light aircraft - whose pilots predominantly fly in accordance with Visual Flight Rules below flight level 195 - are spaced at intervals of 25 Kilohertz (kHz). The voice-communication frequency range is from 118 MHz to 136.975 MHz. This range gives a frequency-spread of 18.975 MHz or 18 975 kHz.

Figure 1.1 VHF Communications and VHF Navigation Sets fitted to a light aircraft.

With channel spacing of 25 kHz, this spread allows 760 distinct frequencies to be selected (118.025, 118.050, 118.075, 118.1, 118.125, and so on). VHF radios in some light aircraft have only 720 channels, and you may even find older radios which operate on only 360 channels. Neither of these latter two types may be used in accordance with the Instrument Flight Rules (IFR). In certain countries, including Germany, 720 Channel and 360 Channel radios are not even permissible for VFR flights.

Even the theoretically possible 760 distinct frequencies available to aircraft fitted with 25 kHz spaced radios have proved too few in congested airspace such as that above Europe. Consequently, within European airspace, each 25 kHz-spaced frequency had to be allocated to Air Traffic Service Units at <u>several</u> locations. But when the same frequency is shared by several ground stations, frequency overlap can occur, as depicted schematically in *Figure 1.2*.

Figure 1.2 VHF Frequency Overlap.

Consequently the sharing of frequencies has to be closely coordinated between nations, and protection areas established within which frequencies cannot be shared. In the areas coloured red, yellow and blue, in *Figure 1.2*, there is no frequency overlap. But in the areas marked with intersecting lines, overlap does occur. So, if the transmitting stations shown in the diagram were serving aircraft operating in the overlap areas, those stations should not use the same VHF voice communication frequency. The higher the altitude the more widespread must be the protection area within which frequencies cannot be shared. In the high density air traffic area of European Upper Airspace, therefore, 760 frequencies were found not to be enough for the management of high-altitude air traffic. More frequencies were required.

So, since the beginning of the 21st Century, Air Traffic Control Services have adopted 8.33kHz spacing between frequencies, in European Upper Airspace.

VHF Voice Communications - 8.33 kHz Frequency Spacing.

As a result of heavy congestion in the ICAO European Upper Airspace Region, then, a frequency spacing of 8.33 kHz was implemented by ICAO, in October 1999, above FL 245. The adoption of 8.33 kHz spacing in the place of 25 kHz spacing increased the number of frequencies available by a factor of 3. By 2002, most European countries had introduced a national requirement that 8.33 kHz frequency spacing be introduced for VHF voice communications in their own Upper Airspace. As a consequence, there is now a mandatory requirement for aircraft operating above Flight Level 245 in European Airspace to carry 8.33 kHz capable radios.

Since March 2007, the 8.33 kHz requirement in European Airspace has applied to airspace above FL 195. It is likely that the requirement for commercial air traffic operating in Upper Airspace to be fitted with 8.33 kHz radios will become global.

Plans have subsequently been formulated to commence introduction of 8.33 kHz spacing below FL 195 from 2012, ensuring that all new radios comply, with full implementation by 2018 for all airspace users.

THE TRANSMISSION OF VHF VOICE COMMUNICATION FREQUENCIES OVER THE RT.

Although radios capable of selecting frequencies at 8.33 kHz spacing are not yet required to be fitted to general aviation aircraft which operate in Lower Airspace, the introduction of 8.33 kHz frequency spacing in Europe above Flight Level 195 has, in one important respect, affected all pilots operating in European skies, even those who fly light aircraft, VFR only, in Lower Airspace.

As already mentioned, 8.33 kHz spacing has increased the number of VHF voice communication frequencies by a factor of 3, making over 2 000 distinct frequencies available, instead of 760, as was the case formerly. In these new circumstances, it has become necessary, with certain exceptions, for every digit of the VHF voice communication frequency to be pronounced when pilots and controllers communicate with one another, instead of abbreviating the frequency designations as had been the practice, until recently, in standard RT phraseology. It is expected that 8.33 kHz spacing, there will have to be 4 digits after the decimal point.

The new phraseology for frequency transmission has been implemented in both Upper and Lower Airspace, in European skies, for all RT communications between pilots and ground stations, irrespective of whether aircraft are required to be fitted with 8.33 kHz radios or not.

The new phraseology is, however, straightforward to learn.

The New Phraseology.

Typically, VHF voice communication frequencies (118 MHz to 136.975 MHz) are expressed in the following formats, depending on whether they consist of whole Megahertz, only, or of Megahertz and Kilohertz:

a.	**119.000 MHz**
b.	**124.600 MHz**
c.	**129.250 MHz**
d.	**130.425 MHz**

With effect from May 2006, throughout Europe, the above frequency formats are to be expressed as indicated below, when speaking over the RT. The pronunciation of the individual digits is in line with conventional RT pronunciation, which will be covered later in this book.

For Frequency Types a and b, where the frequency ends in two or three zeros, <u>the first four digits only</u> are to be transmitted. That is:

- **wun wun niner DAYSEEMAL zero.**
- **wun two fower DAYSEEMAL six.**

For Frequency Types c and d, <u>all six digits</u> are to be transmitted. That is:

- **wun two niner DAYSEEMAL two fife zero.**
- **wun tree zero DAYSEEMAL fower two fife.**

Outside Europe.

For the time being, outside Europe, Frequency Types c and d may still be heard transmitted as five digits only. That is:

- **wun two niner DAYSEEMAL two fife.**
- **wun tree zero DAYSEEMAL fower two.**

DIALLING UP FREQUENCIES ON THE VHF COMMUNICATIONS RADIO.

As the pilot of a light aircraft, flying below Flight Level 195 (19 500 feet measured with respect to the pressure datum of 1013.2 millibars (hectopascal)), your aircraft need not be fitted with an 8.33 kHz capable radio. Nevertheless, you will find that your radio's frequency display shows either five or six digits, as depicted by the radios in *Figure 1.3*.

Figure 1.3 Simple five-digit and six-digit radio displays.

Dialling Up Frequencies on a Radio with a 5-Digit Display.

If your radio has a five-digit display, and you are passed a frequency consisting of four digits (e.g. wun two fife DAYSEEMAL zero [125.0], or wun tree tree DAYSEEMAL niner [133.9]), select the four digits you hear, followed by a zero.

If your radio has a five-digit display, and you are passed a frequency consisting of six digits (e.g. wun two fower DAYSEEMAL fower fife zero [124.450], or wun tree zero DAYSEEMAL fower two fife [130.425]), select the first five digits that you hear, and ignore the sixth digit. Your radio will take care of the sixth digit, automatically.

Outside Europe.

If you are flying outside Europe with a five-digit display radio, and you are passed a frequency consisting of five digits (e.g. wun two fower DAYSEEMAL fower fife [124.45], or wun tree zero DAYSEEMAL fower two [130.42]), simply select all five digits that you hear. Your radio will take care of the sixth digit, automatically.

IN ALL CASES, READ BACK THE FREQUENCY TO THE GROUND STATION, EXACTLY AS YOU HEAR IT.

Dialling Up Frequencies on a Radio with a 6-Digit Display.

If your radio has a six-digit display, and you are passed a frequency consisting of four digits (e.g. wun two fife DAYSEEMAL zero [125.0], or wun tree tree DAYSEEMAL niner [133.9]), select the four digits that you hear, followed by two zeros.

If your radio has a six-digit display and you are passed a frequency consisting of six digits (e.g. wun two fower DAYSEEMAL fower fife zero [124.450], or wun tree zero DAYSEEMAL fower two fife [130.425]), select all six digits that you hear.

You will find, however, if your radio is a 25 kHz-spaced radio, that the sixth digit selects itself, automatically.

If you are flying outside Europe with a six-digit display radio, and you are passed a frequency consisting of five digits (e.g. wun two fower DAYSEEMAL fower fife [124.45], or wun tree zero DAYSEEMAL fower two [130.42]), your radio will probably select the sixth digit itself, if it is a 25 kHz-spaced radio. If it is a 8.33 kHz-spaced radio, however, you will have to select the sixth digit yourself. If the fifth digit is a 5, the sixth digit will be 0. If the fifth digit is any other number than 5 (it will then be either a 7 or a 2), the sixth digit will be 5.

IN ALL CASES, READ BACK THE FREQUENCY TO THE GROUND STATION, EXACTLY AS YOU HEAR IT.

The above account of frequency selection may sound complicated, but, in practice, you will find that the rules are very simple, and that you will soon get used to them.

FREQUENCY DISPLAY AND FREQUENCY SELECTION.

Dual Frequency Selection.

VHF radios, such as those depicted in *Figure 1.3* and *Figure 1.5*, allow the pilot to select only the frequency-in-use, but many modern radios allow frequencies to be pre-selected. The radios illustrated in *Figure 1.4* display both the frequency-in-use and a second frequency which the pilot has pre-selected as a standby frequency.

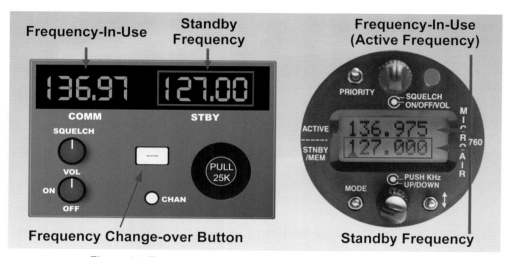

Figure 1.4 Two types of radio with standby-frequency displays.

The standby frequency is usually the frequency that the pilot knows he will require to change to in order to speak to the next ground station, after the service that he is receiving on the current frequency-in-use has been completed. This standby frequency becomes the in-use, or active, frequency when the pilot presses a frequency change-over button. At the same time, the previous in-use frequency becomes the standby frequency. With this type of radio, when the pilot dials up a new frequency using the tuning knobs, it is the standby frequency which becomes the new frequency. The new standby frequency is then ready to become the in-use frequency whenever the pilot wishes.

Single Frequency Displays.

Some radios, with only a single-frequency-display, possess a memory which allows the frequencies a pilot uses most often to be stored and then selected, at will, by switching a frequency-selector knob from one position to another. One of the positions of the frequency-selector knob is reserved for the dialling up of new frequencies, not already stored in the memory. *Figure 1.5* depicts a radio with a single frequency display and able to store 4-frequencies in its memory. With the selector knob at position "A", a new frequency may be dialled up. When the frequency selector knob is then moved to one of the 4 positions, and the white "store" button pressed, the new frequency is stored in the radio's memory, at the position selected.

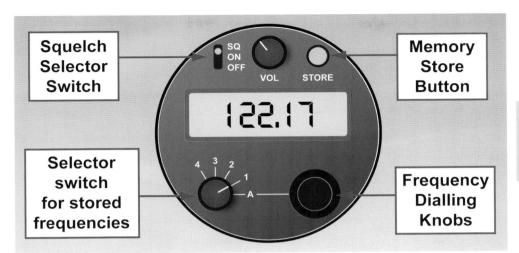

Figure 1.5 A single frequency display radio with a 4-frequency memory.

Make sure that you know how to use all the features on your aircraft's radio set.

The Intercom.

Most light aircraft radios are fitted with an integrated intercom system. If the intercom volume is able to be adjusted independently of the radio reception volume, a correct balance between the intercom and radio volumes should be achieved before take-off. It is important that radio transmissions should be able to be heard above the intercom exchanges between the aircraft's crew members. Make sure that you know how to use all the features of your aircraft's radio set.

The Squelch Control.

Most radio sets have a switch or knob marked squelch. The squelch functions as a kind of filter, muting the receiver audio output when no signal is being received.

In this way, the squelch facility permits the pilot to eliminate the hissing background noise, sometimes referred to as white noise, caused by atmospheric interference. When squelch is selected, either with a switch *(Figure 1.5)* or by turning the squelch control knob *(Figure 1.4, left)*, the muting action of the squelch suppresses the weak signals which cause the interference noise which would otherwise be audible when no signal was being received. With squelch selected, only strong, clear signals from radio transmissions pass through to the pilot's head-set. You should note that if a pilot were communicating with a ground station at maximum transmission range, he may have to deselect squelch in order to improve readability.

If a squelch control knob is fitted to your radio set, as opposed to a simple squelch switch, the correct squelch setting procedure is as follows:

• Set the volume control of the radio set to about half way.

• Turn up the squelch control until the background hiss is heard.

• Turn down the squelch control to the position where the hiss just disappears.

This position will be the correct position for the squelch control knob.

RADIO FREQUENCIES USED IN AVIATION.

The table below shows the division of radio frequencies into the various bands, and their use in aviation. Only the VHF and HF bands are used for radio communications.

Frequencies	Band	Wavelength	Uses
3-30 kHz	VLF (Very Low Frequency)	100 - 10 km	Very long range navigation
30 - 300 kHz	LF (Low Frequency)	10 - 1 km	NDB, Decca, Loran-C
300 - 3000 kHz	MF (Medium Frequency)	1 km - 100 m	NDB
3 - 30 MHz	HF (High Frequency)	100 - 10 m	HF RT
30 - 300 MHz	VHF (Very High Frequency)	10 - 1 m	VHF RT, VDF, VOR, ILS, marker beacons
300 - 3000 MHz	UHF (Ultra High Frequency)	1 m - 10 cm	ILS Glidepath, DME, some surveillance radars
3 - 30 GHz	SHF (Super High Frequency)	10 - 1 cm	PAR, some surveillance radar, radio altimeter
30 - 300 GHz	EHF (Extremely High Frequency)	1 cm - 1 mm	Airfield Surface Movement Radar

The following table shows the frequencies in the **VHF** band which are of concern to the general aviation pilot.

Frequencies	Use
88 - 107.95 MHz	Broadcasting (AM & FM)
108 - 117.975 MHz	Radio Navigation (ILS & VOR)
118 - 136.975 MHz	Radio Communication (This is the band that is used for VHF voice communications)

CHAPTER 2
GENERAL OPERATING PROCEDURES

The title-page photograph for this chapter is reproduced by kind permission of 97 Squadron Association.

INTRODUCTION.

In this chapter you will learn the basic procedures which are common to all radiotelephony (RT) communications. Since RT is the means by which pilots and ground radio operators communicate with each other, it is vital, for reasons of safety and efficiency, that all information and instructions are transmitted correctly.

Standard RT phraseology and procedures are used to reduce the possibility of misunderstandings.

In all RT communications, therefore, standard phraseology and procedures have been agreed, and are used worldwide to reduce the possibility of misunderstandings. Consequently, it is vitally important that all pilots learn and understand standard RT phraseology and procedures, and that pilots get into the habit of using them at all times. You should be aware that many accidents and incidents have occurred because of the misunderstanding caused by the use of non-standard RT procedures and/or phraseology.

In RT, the most important consideration is that messages should be transmitted and received clearly, and unambiguously. Messages should also be kept as brief as possible, though they must be complete.

Many aircraft accidents and incidents have occured because of misunderstandings arising from the use of non-standard RT phraseology and procedures.

RT TRANSMISSION TECHNIQUES.

Positioning the Microphone.

Figure 2.1 Here, the microphone is too far from the pilot's lips.

The headset should be adjusted so that it sits comfortably on the pilot's head with the band joining the earphones centrally placed on top of the head. The earphones can be moved up or down so that they fit the ears snugly, with the ears in the centre of each padded earphone.

In order that the pilot's RT transmissions may be heard clearly by a ground station operator, and other pilots on the same RT frequency, it is important that the pilot places his microphone in the correct position.

If the microphone is too far away from the pilot's lips, the speech volume will be reduced and the microphone will pick up extraneous noise from the cockpit, making the pilot's message difficult to discern.

Figure 2.2 Here, the microphone is too close to the pilot's lips.

If the microphone is too close to the pilot's lips, the pilot's speech will be distorted.

Figure 2.3 The correct microphone position.

The correct microphone position is shown in *Figure 2.3*. The microphone is about ¾ inch (2 cm) from the lips.

The microphone should be positioned opposite the centre of the mouth.

The boom should be secure so that it will not move if the pilot moves his head suddenly or if the aircraft meets with turbulence.

Before transmitting, listen out.

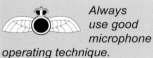
Always use good microphone operating technique.

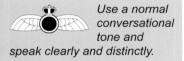
Use a normal conversational tone and speak clearly and distinctly.

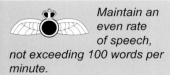
Maintain an even rate of speech, not exceeding 100 words per minute.

Maintain the speaking volume at a constant level.

Basic Rules for Transmitting.

The following considerations should be borne in mind whenever you transit over the RT.

1. When using a new frequency, listen out for about 5 seconds before transmitting. If an RT exchange is ongoing, make sure it has been completed.

2. When transmitting, use your normal voice; do not force your speech or mumble.

3. Maintain an even rate of speech, not exceeding 100 words per minute.

4. Do not raise your voice, even if you are putting out an emergency message. By speaking too loudly, your words are likely to be distorted for the recipient of your message.

5. RT transmissions containing numbers and letters must be pronounced using RT conventions which will be covered in this chapter. A slight pause before and after numbers will assist in making them easier to understand.

6.   Avoid using hesitation sounds such as 'um', 'er' and 'ah'. To avoid this, think about what you are going to say before transmitting.

Make sure you know what you are going to say before you press the transmit button.

7.   Ensure that you press the transmit button <u>before</u> you begin to speak and that you release the button fully, immediately <u>after</u> your transmission has ended.

Depress the transmit button fully before speaking and release it immediately after the message is complete.

TRANSMISSION OF LETTERS.

When transmitting individual letters, the Phonetic Alphabet is used. The Phonetic Alphabet, given in the table below, consists of words which, by international agreement, are spoken to identify the initial letter of the word. In the table below, you should stress the syllables which are <u>underlined</u>. Note that the words of the Phonetic Alphabet are <u>not</u> always pronounced in the same way as in standard English.

Letter	Phonetic Alphabet	PRONOUNCED
A	alpha	<u>AL</u>-FAH
B	bravo	<u>BRAH</u>-<u>VOH</u>
C	charlie	<u>CHAR</u>-LEE
D	delta	<u>DELL</u>-TAH
E	echo	<u>ECK</u>-OH
F	foxtrot	<u>FOKS</u>-TROT
G	golf	<u>GOLF</u>
H	hotel	HOH-<u>TELL</u>
I	India	<u>IN</u>-DEE-AH
J	juliet	JEW-LEE-<u>ETT</u>
K	kilo	<u>KEY</u>-LOH
L	lima	<u>LEE</u>-MAH
M	mike	<u>MIKE</u>
N	november	NO-<u>VEM</u>-BER
O	oscar	<u>OSS</u>-CAR
P	papa	<u>PAH</u>-PAH
Q	quebec	KEH-<u>BECK</u>
R	romeo	<u>ROW</u>-ME-OH
S	sierra	SEE-<u>AIR</u>-RAH
T	tango	<u>TANG</u>-GO
U	uniform	<u>YOU</u>-NEE-FORM
V	victor	<u>VIK</u>-TAH
W	whiskey	<u>WISS</u>-KEY
X	x-ray	<u>ECKS</u>-RAY
Y	yankee	<u>YANG</u>-KEY
Z	zulu	<u>ZOO</u>-LOO

TRANSMISSION OF NUMBERS.

In radiotelephony, individual numbers are pronounced in the manner indicated in the table below. With certain exceptions all numbers should be transmitted by pronouncing each digit separately. <u>Underlined</u> syllables should be emphasised.

Number	Pronunciation
0	<u>ZE</u>-<u>RO</u>
1	<u>WUN</u>
2	<u>TOO</u>
3	<u>TREE</u>
4	<u>FOW</u>-ER
5	<u>FIFE</u>
6	<u>SIX</u>
7	<u>SEV</u>-EN
8	<u>AIT</u>
9	<u>NIN</u>-ER
10	WUN ZERO
75	S<u>EV</u>EN FIFE
583	FIFE AIT TREE
38 143	TREE AIT WUN <u>FOW</u>-ER TREE
Decimal	<u>DAYSEEMAL</u>
Hundred	<u>HUN</u>-DRED
Thousand	<u>TOUSAND</u>

Numbers with Digits Pronounced Separately.
Below is a list of the types of aviation information for which numbers must be pronounced using individual digits.

Aircraft Call-signs.

Aircraft Call-sign	Transmitted as
CCA 237	Air China <u>TOO</u>-TREE <u>SEV</u>-EN
OAL 342	Olympic TREE <u>FOW</u>-ER TOO

Flight Levels.

Flight Levels	Transmitted as
FL 150	Flight Level WUN FIFE ZERO
FL 200	Flight Level TOO ZERO ZERO*

*   Note: In the <u>United Kingdom</u>, Flight Levels referring to whole hundreds are pronounced using the word <u>HUN</u>-DRED. For example, FL 200 is pronounced "Flight Level <u>TOO</u> <u>HUN</u>-DRED" and FL 300 is pronounced "Flight Level <u>TREE</u> <u>HUN</u>-DRED."

Headings.

Headings	Transmitted as
Heading 100°	Heading WUN ZERO ZERO
Heading 346°	Heading TREE FOW-ER SIX
Heading 045°	Heading ZERO FOW-ER FIFE

Wind direction and speed.

Wind direction and speed	Transmitted as
Wind 230° 20 Knots	Wind TOO TREE ZERO degrees TOO ZERO knots
Wind 080° 12 Knots	Wind ZERO AIT ZERO degrees WUN TOO knots
Gusting 25	Gusting TOO FIFE

Transponder Codes.

Transponder Codes	Transmitted as
Squawk 2400	SQUAWK TOO FOW-ER ZERO ZERO
Squawk 4215	SQUAWK FOW-ER TOO WUN FIFE

Runway Designations.

Runway	Transmitted as
Runway 27	Runway TOO SEV-EN
Runway 14	Runway WUN FOW-ER

Altimeter subscale settings.

Altimeter Settings	Transmitted as
QNH 998	QNH NINER NINER AIT
QNH 1000	QNH WUN ZERO ZERO ZERO

Frequencies.

Frequency	Transmitted as
118.1	WUN WUN AIT DAYSEEMAL WUN
120.375	WUN TOO ZERO DAYSEEMAL TREE SEV-EN FIFE

The frequency 131.125, when passed over the RT, is spoken as: WUN TREE WUN DAYSEEMAL WUN TOO FIFE.

Numbers which contain a **decimal point**, such as **radio frequencies** or **radio-navigation frequencies**, are transmitted with the decimal point in the normal place. The word **decimal** is pronounced **"DAYSEEMAL"**.

Exceptions to the Above Rule.
The exceptions to the rule that digits be pronounced individually are numbers used in the transmission of **Altitude**, **Height**, **Visibility** and **Runway Visual Range Information**, which contain <u>whole hundreds</u> and <u>whole thousands</u>.

These numbers should be transmitted by pronouncing **each digit in the number of hundreds or thousands**, followed by the word **hundred**, or **thousand** as appropriate, as illustrated by the following tables.

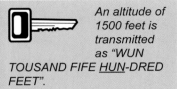

An altitude of 1500 feet is transmitted as "WUN TOUSAND FIFE HUN-DRED FEET".

Altitude.

Altitude	Transmitted as
700 feet	SEV-EN HUN-DRED FEET
4500 feet	FOW-ER TOUSAND FIFE HUN-DRED FEET

But:

1450 feet	WUN FOW-ER FIFE ZERO FEET

Cloud Height.

Cloud Height	Transmitted as
2200 feet	TOO TOUSAND TOO HUN-DRED FEET
3600 feet	TREE TOUSAND SIX HUN-DRED FEET

Visibility.

Visibility	Transmitted as
Visibility 1000 metres	VISIBILITY WUN TOUSAND METRES
Visibility 600 metres	VISIBILITY SIX HUN-DRED METRES

Runway Visual Range.

Runway Visual Range	Transmitted as	
RVR 700	RVR SEV-EN HUN-DRED	
RVR 1500	RVR WUN TOUSAND FIFE HUN-DRED	

TRANSMISSION OF TIME.

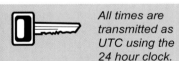

All times are transmitted as UTC using the 24 hour clock.

When transmitting time, Co-ordinated Universal Time (UTC) is used, based on the 24 hour clock, and is sometimes referred to as GMT or Zulu time. UTC is the standard time reference used throughout the aviation world. When transmitting time, controllers and pilots give the minutes only, unless there is likely to be confusion, in which case the hour should be given too. Time checks are given to the nearest minute and preceded by the word 'TIME'.

Time	Transmitted as	
0803	ZERO TREE, or ZERO AIT ZERO TREE	
1300	ONE TREE ZERO ZERO	
2057	FIFE SEV-EN, or TWO ZERO FIFE SEV-EN	

AERONAUTICAL GROUND STATION CALL-SIGNS.

Aeronautical ground stations are identified by the name of the station followed by a suffix which indicates the type of service being provided by the ground station. A table containing the most common suffixes is given below. In most cases, the service being provided is obvious from the suffix. The meanings of the suffixes are explained in other volumes in this Oxford Aviation Academy series of text books.

The suffixes given in this lesson are from the ICAO Manual of Radiotelephony (Doc 9432). However, there may be some minor differences among JAA/EASA member nations. Pilots are, therefore, advised to consult their national RT manuals to ensure that they are aware of any differences.

Unit or Service	Call-sign Suffix	Example
Area Control Centre	**CONTROL**	**Stansted Control**
Radar (in general)	**RADAR**	**Bremen Radar**
Approach Control	**APPROACH**	**Birmingham Approach**
Aerodrome Control	**TOWER**	**Munich Tower**
Surface Movement Control	**GROUND**	**Brize Norton Ground**
Direction Finding Station	**HOMER**	**Hawarden Homer**
Flight Information Service	**INFORMATION**	**Goodwood Information**
Air-Ground Communications Service	**RADIO**	**Leicester Radio**

The initial call to a station must include the ground station name. For example, if you wish to contact aerodrome control at Stansted airport you would call

STANSTED TOWER.

However, once you have established satisfactory two-way communications with Stansted Tower, the suffix may be omitted in subsequent calls; but only after the ground station, itself, has initiated the omission.

Figure 2.4 Oxford Tower.

AIRCRAFT CALL-SIGNS.

There are three types of aircraft call-sign.

Type 1.

The first type of call-sign is the ICAO registration marking of the aircraft. For example:

G-TAGS (GOLF-TANGO-ALPHA-GOLF-SIERRA)

Figure 2.5 G-TAGS.

Type 2.

The second type of call-sign is made up of the radiotelephony designator of the aircraft operating company, followed by the last four characters of the ICAO registration marking of the aircraft. For example:

OXBOW DCBA

Type 3.

The third type of aircraft call-sign consists of the radiotelephony designator of the aircraft operating company, followed by the **flight number identification**. For example:

OXBOW 246

Figure 2.6 Oxbow 246.

Abbreviated call-signs have the following form:

Type 1.   The first character of the registration, followed by the last two characters of the call-sign. For example:

G-GS (GOLF-GOLF SIERRA)

Type 2.   The radiotelephony designator of the aircraft operating agency followed by the last two characters of the call-sign. For example:

OXBOW BRAVO ALPHA

Type 3.   There is no abbreviation for this type of call-sign.

ESTABLISHING COMMUNICATIONS WITH A GROUND STATION.

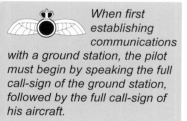

When first establishing communications with a ground station, the pilot must begin by speaking the full call-sign of the ground station, followed by the full call-sign of his aircraft.

When establishing communication with a ground station, an aircraft must first pronounce the full call sign of the ground station followed by its own full call-sign. After satisfactory communication has been established an aircraft may use an abbreviated call sign, only after it has been instigated by the ground station.

If the pilot wishes any kind of service from the ground station, he must make his request in the initial call.

Below, we give an example of an exchange between an aircraft establishing communications with an Air Traffic Control Unit at an aerodrome.

 Walden Tower, G-ABCD, Request joining instructions.

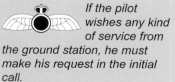

If the pilot wishes any kind of service from the ground station, he must make his request in the initial call.

G-ABCD, Walden Tower, Go ahead*.

G-ABCD, Cessna 172, From Rissington Parva to Walden, 10 miles North of Walden, 2 500 feet.

An aircraft may use an abbreviated call-sign only when the abbreviation has first been used by the ground station.

G-CD, Join downwind, Runway 20, Wind 195 degrees, 5 knots, QNH 1003, Call when downwind.

Runway 20, QNH 1003, Wilco, G-CD.

CONTINUATION OF ESTABLISHED COMMUNICATIONS.

Position of Call-sign.
Within an established RT exchange between an aircraft and a ground station, the aircraft call-sign should be positioned as follows:

From Ground Station to Aircraft.
The ground station will always begin the transmission of a message to an aircraft by pronouncing the full or abbreviated call-sign of the aircraft addressed. This is so that the pilot is alerted to listen to the ground station's message or to the ground station's reply to the pilot's message.

G-CD, Line up, Runway 20.

From Aircraft to Ground Station.
Case 1: When replying, acknowledging, or reading back information, the pilot puts the aircraft call-sign at the end of the message.

Lining up, Runway 20, G-CD.

Case 2: However, if several minutes elapse between receiving an instruction from a ground station, (between, say, an instruction to report reaching a position or level, and the aircraft actually arriving at that position or level), the pilot will begin his call with his call-sign. Consequently, the pilot's report to the ground station that he has arrived at the position or level is regarded as a further <u>initial</u> call, rather than the continuation of an established communication.

* Note: In the United Kingdom, the ICAO standard phrase, "Go Ahead", is replaced by the phrase, "Pass your message".

G-CD, Join downwind, Runway 20, Wind 195 degrees, 5 knots, QNH 1003, Call when downwind.

Runway 20, QNH 1003, Wilco, G-CD.

Several minutes later:

G-CD, Downwind.

The following example summarises the principle of **call-sign placement**. Note how the position of the call-sign changes in the transmissions from the aircraft, but remains the same in the ground-station transmissions.

G-CD, Report airfield in sight.

Wilco, G-CD.

Several minutes later:

G-CD, Airfield in sight.

G-CD, Report right base, Runway 26.

Immediate reply:

Report right base, Runway 26, G-CD.

Several minutes later:

G-CD, Right base, Runway 26.

Say Again.

If there is doubt that a message has been correctly received, a repetition of the message may be requested, either in full or in part, by pronouncing the phrase, **"Say Again"**.

 G-CD, Right base to land, Runway 24.

 G-CD, Say again.

 G-CD, Right base to land, Runway 24.

When a station is called but is uncertain of the identity of the calling station, the calling station should be requested to "**say again your call-sign**".

 Georgetown Approach, Golf Foxtrot Hotel Juliet Mike, Request Flight Information Service

 Station calling Georgetown Approach, Say again your call-sign.

 Georgetown Approach, Golf Foxtrot Hotel Juliet Mike.

Correction.

When an error is made in a transmission, the word **'CORRECTION'** is spoken, and then the correct version transmitted.

 Morcroft Approach, G-ABCD, Estimating Westcott at 43, Correction Westcott at 46.

If a correction can best be made by repeating the entire message, the phrase

'**CORRECTION I SAY AGAIN**' may be used before transmitting the whole message a second time.

Words Twice.
When it is considered that reception may be difficult, important elements of the message may be spoken twice.

Standby.
The expression **"standby"** means that a station, having received a message, is too busy to respond to the initial call, but will call the station back as soon as it can. No reply should be given on receipt of **"standby"**.

Walden Ground, G-FHJM, PA28, At the light aircraft parking area, Two POB, For VFR local flight, Request taxi instruction.

G-FHJM, standby.

"Standby" may also be used in order to alert a station to the fact that it needs to be prepared to receive some information that it may wish to record.

G-IK, Standby for Walden weather.

G-IK.

TRANSFER OF COMMUNICATIONS.

When Under Air Traffic Control.
When an aircraft is **under air traffic control**, the **Air Traffic Control Unit (ATCU)** will sometimes require an aircraft to change from one frequency to another. The **RT phraseology** for this situation is given below.

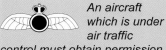

An aircraft which is under air traffic control must obtain permission from the ATCU before the pilot may change frequency.

G-IK, Contact Walden Approach, 129.1.

Contact Walden Approach, 129.1, G-IK.

An aircraft which is under the control of an **ATCU** must obtain permission from the **ATCU** before the pilot may change frequency.

When Not Under Air Traffic Control.

If an aircraft is **not under air traffic control**, but is in contact with a ground station (say, receiving a **Flight Information Service** or speaking to an **Air-Ground Radio Operator**), the pilot must notify the ground station of his intention to change frequency.

Norton Radio, G-IK, Changing to Walden Tower, 129.1.

G-IK, Roger.

RADIO TEST PROCEDURES.

At the beginning of a flight, usually before taxiing, or if the pilot is or becomes unsure about the serviceability of his radio, he may make a radio test transmission.

Test transmissions should take the following form:

- The **call-sign** or **identifier** of the station being called.

- The aircraft **call-sign**.

- The words **'RADIO CHECK'**.

- The **frequency** being used.

Replies to test transmissions by ground stations should be as follows:

- The **call-sign** of the aircraft requesting the check.

- The **call-sign** of the station replying.

- Information regarding the **readability** of the transmission.

Readability Scale.

The readability of transmissions should be classified in accordance with the scale of readability given below. Usually, the number, **1**, **2**, **3**, **4** or **5** is preceded by the words **"Read you"** or **"Readability"**.

1 = Unreadable.

2 = Readable now and then.

3 = Readable but with difficulty.

4 = Readable.

5 = Perfectly readable.

Stephenville Tower, G-ABCD, Radio check, 118.9.

G-ABCD, Stephenville Tower, Read you 5.

Stephenville Tower, G-ABCD, Radio check, 118.9.

G-ABCD, Stephenville Tower, Readability 3, Loud background whistle.

THE Q CODE.

The **Q code** is a standardised collection of 3-letter message encodings. All **Q-codes** begin with the letter **Q**. The codes were initially developed for wireless telegraphy communications, using Morse Code, but they continue to be used today, in voice transmissions.

Depicted in *Figures 2.7 to 2.11* are the most common aviation **Q codes** which remain in use in current **ICAO radio telephony phraseology**.

When **Q codes** are spoken on the radio, they are pronounced as alphabet letters in normal English, not in accordance with the **Phonetic Alphabet**.

QDM.

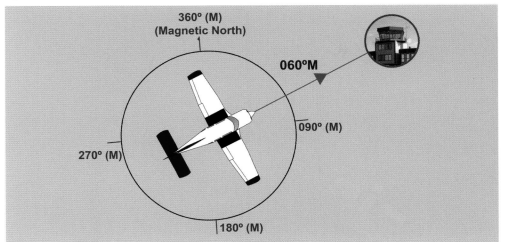

Figure 2.7 QDM.

QDM is the magnetic bearing *to* fly to a station.
If there is no wind, the QDM would be the heading to fly to reach the VDF station. With a wind blowing, a wind correction angle has to be applied to the QDM to obtain the heading to fly.

The **QDM** is the **MAGNETIC bearing** from the aircraft <u>to</u> the transmitting station. In this example, the **QDM** is **060° (M)**. If there were no wind, the **QDM** would be the heading that the aircraft would fly to reach the transmitting station. When there <u>is</u> a wind, a **wind correction angle** must be applied to the **QDM** to obtain the **heading to steer**.

QDR.

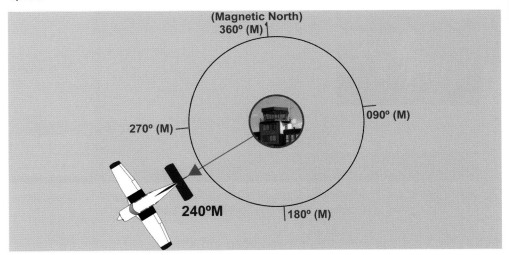

Figure 2.8 QDR.

QDR is the magnetic bearing *from* a station.

The **QDR** is the **MAGNETIC bearing** of the aircraft <u>from</u> the transmitting station. In this example, the **QDR** is **240° (M)**.

QTE.

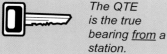

The QTE is the true bearing *from* a station.

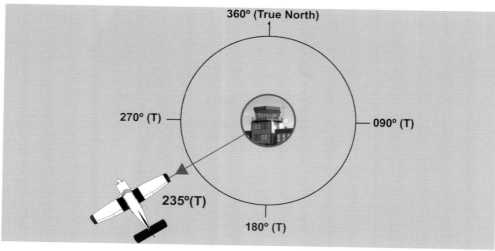

Figure 2.9 QTE.

The **QTE** is the **TRUE bearing** of the aircraft *from* the transmitting station. In this case, the **QTE** is **235° (T)**.

QFE.

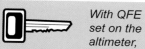

With QFE set on the altimeter, an aircraft, in flight, reports its vertical separation from the airfield pressure datum as 'height'.

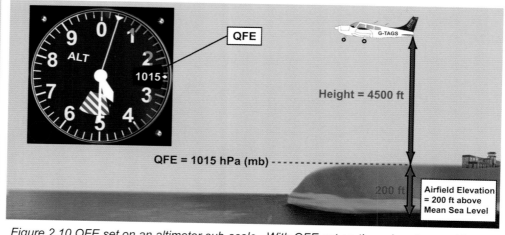

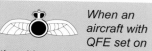

When an aircraft with QFE set on the altimeter is on the ground at the airfield, the altimeter indicates zero.

Figure 2.10 QFE set on an altimeter sub-scale. With QFE set on the subscale, an altimeter reads height above airfield level, when the aircraft is airborne.

QFE is the observed pressure at a **specified airfield datum** (usually the runway threshold or highest point on the airfield) corrected for temperature. **QFE** is most often used as the altimeter setting for local flying. With **QFE** in the altimeter subscale, the altimeter shows the **height** of the aircraft above the airfield datum. With **QFE** set on the altimeter, the aircraft reports its vertical separation from the ground as **height**. (See Figure 2.10.)

With **QFE** set, the altimeter will read zero when the aircraft is on the ground, at the aerodrome.

QNH.

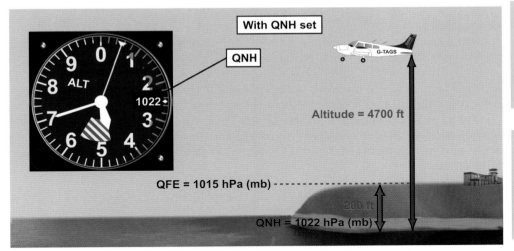

With QNH set on the altimeter, an aircraft, in flight, reports its vertical separation from sea-level as 'altitude'.

When an aircraft with airfield QNH set on its altimeter is on the ground at the airfield, the altimeter indicates the elevation of the airfield.

With QNH set

QNH

ALT

1022

Altitude = 4700 ft

QFE = 1015 hPa (mb)

200 ft

QNH = 1022 hPa (mb)

Figure 2.11 With QNH set on the subscale, the altimeter reads altitude above mean sea level, when the aircraft is airborne

Airfield **QNH** is the observed pressure at the airfield, reduced to its **sea-level value**. Consequently, with **QNH** set in the altimeter subscale, the altimeter indicates the **vertical separation of the aircraft from sea-level**. When the aircraft is airborne, with **QNH** set on the altimeter, the aircraft reports its vertical separation from sea-level as **altitude**. *(See Figure 2.11.)*

When the aircraft is on the ground, at an airfield, with **QNH** set on the altimeter, the altimeter indicates the **elevation** of the airfield.

CATEGORIES OF RT MESSAGES.

By convention, **RT messages** are placed into categories so that messages can be dealt with in order of **priority**. **RT messages** have the following order of **priority**:

1. **Distress Messages**: Messages relating to an aircraft which is threatened by **serious and/or imminent danger** and which requires **immediate assistance**. (A **distress call** is prefixed by the words "**Mayday, Mayday, Mayday**".)

2. **Urgency Messages**: Messages relating to the safety of an aircraft, or other vehicle, or of a person on board the aircraft, where immediate assistance is not required. (An urgency message is prefixed by the words: "**Pan Pan**, **Pan Pan**, **Pan Pan**".)

3. **Direction Finding Messages**: Communications relating to direction finding.

4. **Flight Safety Messages**: Messages to the pilot of an aircraft concerning the safety of the aircraft.

5. **Meteorological Messages**: Weather reports, forecasts and warnings.

6. **Flight Regularity Messages**: Messages regarding the operation or maintenance of ground facilities, the servicing of aircraft etc.

CLEARANCES AND READBACK REQUIREMENTS.

Clearances.

A **clearance** may vary in content from a brief **clearance** to take-off or land, to a detailed description of the route that an aircraft is to fly.

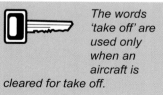

The words 'take off' are used only when an aircraft is cleared for take off.

Air traffic controllers will pass a route **clearance** slowly and clearly, because the pilot may need to write it down. Whenever possible, a **route clearance** should be passed to an aircraft before start up. In any case, controllers should avoid passing a **clearance** to a pilot engaged in complicated taxiing manoeuvres, and on no occasion should a **clearance** be passed when the pilot is engaged in line-up or take-off manoeuvres.

The following exchange between **ATC** and **G-ABCD** is an example of a simple **VFR route clearance**.

G-ABCD, Cleared to control zone boundary via Hartlade*, VFR, Not above 1300ft, QNH 1005, After departure climb straight ahead to 1000ft before turning right, Squawk 5501.

Air Traffic Control clearances must be read back by the pilot, word for word.

Cleared to control zone boundary via Hartlade, VFR, Not above 1300ft, QNH 1005, After departure climb straight ahead to 1000ft before turning right, Squawk 5501, G-ABCD.

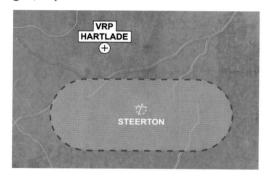

Figure 2.12.

Pilots must be aware that an air traffic **clearance** is NOT an instruction to **take off** or to **enter an active runway**. The words **TAKE OFF** are used <u>only</u> when an aircraft is given **clearance to take off**, or when cancelling a **take-off clearance**. At other times, the words **DEPARTURE** or **AIRBORNE** are used.

Controllers will expect pilots to comply with **clearances** and **instructions** as promptly as is commensurate with flight safety and normal aircraft operating procedures. Pilots should inform controllers if, for any reason, they are unable to comply with a **clearance** or **instruction**. If a high degree of urgency dictates that a **clearance** should be complied with without any delay, the controller will use the words "**immediately**" or "**now**". "**Immediately**" expresses a high degree of urgency.

The Conditional Clearance.

The **conditional clearance** is a **clearance** where **a condition** must be met before the **clearance** may be acted upon. **Conditional clearances** are covered in **Chapter 4**, **Aerodrome Control**.

* Note: Hartlade would be a Visual Reference Point. (See Figure 2.12.)

Read-back requirements.

Air Traffic Control clearances and **RT messages** which directly affect __flight safety__ must be **read back** by the pilot, word for word. By **reading back** a **clearance**, for instance, the controller is able to tell whether the **clearance** has been correctly understood by the pilot, and also that the **clearance** has been transmitted as intended. A **read-back** also confirms to the controller that the correct aircraft, and only that aircraft, will take action on the **clearance**.

G-ABCD, Cleared to enter Control Zone on your present track, Maintain 2 500 feet, QNH 987.

Cleared to enter Control Zone on present track, Maintain 2 500 feet, QNH 987, G-ABCD.

G-JM, Line up and wait, Runway 20.

Line up and wait, Runway 20, G-JM.

In general, __all__ **clearances** issued by **Air Traffic Services** must be read back.

The **ICAO Manual of Radiotelephony** stipulates that the following **clearances**, **instructions** and **information** must always be **read back** by the pilot.

- ATC route clearances.

- Clearances and instructions to:

    - enter a runway.

    - land on a runway.

    - take off from a runway.

    - hold short of a runway.

    - cross a runway.

    - back-track on a runway.

- Runway-in-use.

- Altimeter settings.

- Transponder (SSR) codes.

- Level instructions.

- Heading instructions.

- Speed instructions.

- Transition levels.

In the **United Kingdom**, the following additional messages and instructions must also be read back:

- Taxi instructions.

- Approach clearances.

- Very High Frequency Direction Finding Information.

- Frequency changes.

- Type of radar service.

If an aircraft **read-back** of a **clearance**, **instruction** or other item of information is incorrect, the controller will transmit the word '**NEGATIVE**' followed by the correct version of the message.

 QNH 1002, G-JM.

 G-JM, Negative, QNH 992.

 QNH 992, G-JM.

If, at any time, a pilot receives a clearance or instruction that he cannot comply with, the pilot should advise the controller using the phrase 'UNABLE', and give the reason why he cannot comply.

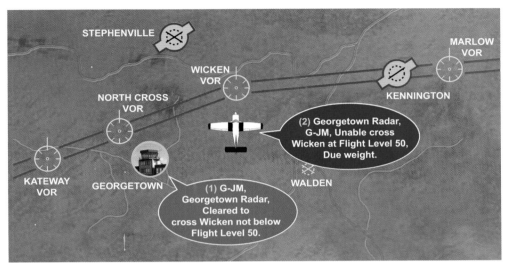

Figure 2.13.

CHAPTER 3
GENERAL PHRASEOLOGY

STANDARD RT WORDS AND PHRASES.

Standard phraseology has been agreed between ICAO member states to avoid ambiguity in RT Communications.

As a direct result of aircraft accidents, RT phraseology has been progressively modified to avoid any possibility of ambiguity or confusion. Specific phrases have well defined meanings and, therefore, should not be modified by the pilot when transmitting.

The table below contains standard words and phrases which are internationally recognised. When used correctly, these standard words and phrases reduce the length of radio transmissions.

The phraseology in the table is standard ICAO phraseology, except where indicated as phraseology used in the United Kingdom only.

The golden rule of good RT practice is to know what you are going to say before you say it.

Word/Phrase	Meaning
ACKNOWLEDGE	"Let me know that you have received and understood this message." This word at the end of a message is used by ATC so that the controller can be sure that the pilot has received and understood the message. Do not, therefore, acknowledge the message unless you do understand it. If you do not fully understand a transmission, ask the ground station to repeat it.
AFFIRM	"Yes." This is a simple response to any question which requires "Yes" as an answer.
APPROVED	"Permission for proposed action is granted." This would normally be used in response to non-standard requests; for example a request to turn in a non-standard direction after take-off.
BREAK	"I hereby indicate the separation between parts of my message". This expression is most commonly used in busy air traffic environments where controllers will speak to two or more aircraft in succession, without releasing the transmit button. You need to be alert to hear your call-sign in these conditions, because of the wide variety of messages being passed to other aircraft.
BREAK BREAK	"I hereby indicate the separation between messages transmitted to different aircraft in a very busy environment."

Internationally agreed, standard RT phraseology almost always has a well defined meaning. Pilots should not, therefore, modify these standard phrases.

The golden rule of good RT practice is to know what you are going to say, before you say it.

CANCEL	"Annul the previously transmitted clearance". This word will be used to cancel any clearance.
CHANGING TO (UNITED KINGDOM ONLY)	"I intend to call a specific unit on a specific frequency." When making this call, you should give the name of the air traffic services unit as well as the frequency to which you intend to change.
CHECK	"Examine a system or procedure (no answer is normally expected)." Although a reply is not normally expected, this should not deter you from making a reply if you feel it would be appropriate.
CLEARED	"Authorised to proceed under the conditions specified." It is important that you understand the specified conditions of the clearance. If you do not, you should ask the controller to repeat them.
CLIMB (UNITED KINGDOM ONLY)	"Climb and maintain." Note that, having instructed you to climb to a particular altitude or flight level, the controller will expect you to maintain it until you request a change, or you are instructed to change.
CONFIRM	"I request verification of ..." An example of a situation where you might use this word is where you have received a clearance and you wish to confirm part of the information before you repeat it in full.
CONTACT	"Establish communication with ...." You would normally be given both the name of the air traffic services unit to be called as well as the frequency.
CORRECT	"That is true", or "That is accurate." In other words, the information you have passed is correct. Not to be confused with "Affirm."
CORRECTION	"An error has been made in this transmission. The correct version is ......"
DESCEND (UNITED KINGDOM ONLY)	"Descend and maintain." The same assumptions apply to this word as to **Climb**.
DISREGARD	"Ignore". The normal response to an RT call telling you to "Disregard the previous message" would normally be "Roger".
FREECALL (UNITED KINGDOM ONLY)	"Call a specified unit. Your details have not been passed" – This expression is used by military units in the UK. When you call the new unit, you must be prepared to pass your flight details.

GO AHEAD	"Proceed with your message."
HOW DO YOU READ	"What is the readability of my transmission." In other words "How clearly can you hear and understand my transmission?"
I SAY AGAIN	"I repeat for clarity or emphasis."
MONITOR	"Listen out on a specific frequency." If you are asked by Air Traffic Control to monitor a frequency, it means that you should listen out on that frequency.
NEGATIVE	"No" or "Permission not granted" or "That is not correct." Notice that, whereas the word **Affirm** can only mean Yes, **Negative** has three distinct meanings which depend on the context of the message being responded to.
OUT	"This exchange of transmissions is ended and no response is expected." This word is normally omitted in VHF transmissions.
OVER	"My transmission is ended and I expect a response from you." Again this word is normally omitted in VHF transmissions.
PASS YOUR MESSAGE (UNITED KINGDOM ONLY)	This expression is synonymous with the ICAO phrase: **Go Ahead**.
READ BACK	"Repeat all, or the specified part, of this message back to me exactly as received." This expression will be used when a controller wants positive confirmation that you have received the message correctly.
RECLEARED (NOT USED IN THE UNITED KINGDOM)	"A change has been made to your last clearance and this new clearance supersedes your previous clearance, or part thereof."
REPORT	"Pass the following information." A typical example of the use of this word would be where you are receiving a Flight Information Service on a VFR cross country flight and the controller asks you to report at a specified Visual Reference Point.
REQUEST	"I should like to know …", "I wish to obtain..." This word is very common in RT transmissions; for example a pilot frequently requests airfield weather or the QNH.
ROGER	"I have received all your last transmission." Under no circumstances should ROGER be used in reply to a question requiring a "READ BACK" or a direct answer in the affirmative (AFFIRM) or negative (NEGATIVE).

The word ROGER means: I have received all of your last transmission.

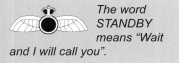

The word STANDBY means "Wait and I will call you".

SAY AGAIN	"Repeat all, or the following part, of your last transmission."
SPEAK SLOWER	"Reduce your rate of speech."
STANDBY	"Wait and I will call you." This is a widely misunderstood word in RT terminology. When you make a call to a controller and he replies by telling you to **Standby**, he does not expect a reply. It means that he is too busy to respond to your initial call and will call you as soon as he can.
UNABLE	"I cannot comply with your request, instruction or clearance."
WILCO	"I understand your message and will comply with it." When you respond to a message with **Wilco** you are telling the controller that you not only understand what you have just been told but that you will carry out any instructions which you may have been given.
WORDS TWICE	As a request: "Communication is difficult. Please send every word twice" or as information: "Since communication is difficult, every word in this message will be sent twice".

ABBREVIATIONS.

Some abbreviations have, by virtue of their common usage, become part of aviation terminology. Some of the more common abbreviations are listed below:

Abbreviation	Meaning
ILS	Instrument Landing System.
QNH	Altimeter Setting to give Vertical Distance above Sea Level.
QFE	Altimeter Setting to give Vertical Distance above the surface of an aerodrome.
RVR	Runway Visual Range.
ADF	Automatic Direction Finding.
ATC	Air Traffic Control.
CAVOK (pronounced KAV-O.K.)	Ceiling and Visibility O.K.
ETA & ETD	Estimated Time of Arrival/Departure.
VFR & IFR	Visual Flight Rules / Instrument Flight Rules.
VOR	VHF Omni-Directional Range.
VHF & UHF	Very High Frequency / Ultra High Frequency.

The abbreviations are spoken using the alphabet pronunciation of their constituent letters rather than the phonetic alphabet.

WORDS WHICH MAY BE OMITTED.

The words listed below may be omitted from transmissions, provided that their omission does not result in ambiguity or confusion.

Word	Context
Surface	In relation to surface wind, speed and direction.
Degrees	In relation to RADAR headings.
Visibility, Cloud, Height	In meteorological reports.
Hectopascal/Millibars*	When giving pressure settings.

(*Note: In the United Kingdom, the unit "millibars" has been retained in preference to Hectopascal. The Hectopascal and the millibar are numerically equal. For example, 1013 millibars is the same pressure as 1013 Hectopascal.)

In the United Kingdom, too, the word "millibars" is included when transmitting pressures of less than 1000 millibars. For example: QNH 998 millibars; QNH 1003.)

Pilots should also avoid the use of courtesies. It is natural for people to wish to sound friendly over the RT and you will hear 'Good morning', 'Good night', 'Hello', etc, being used frequently. In general, however, these courtesies should not be used, particularly in a busy RT environment.

LEVEL INSTRUCTIONS.

Level instructions refer to clearances and reports pertaining to heights, altitude and flight levels.

The precise phraseology used in the transmission and acknowledgement of climb and descent clearances will vary, depending on the circumstances, traffic density and the nature of the flight operations.

Levels may be reported as altitude, height or flight levels according to the phase of flight and the altimeter setting.

(Note: In the United Kingdom, there are some minor differences from the ICAO phraseology when reporting climbing to or descending from heights, altitudes and flight levels. These differences are covered in Chapter 13.)

G-IK, Report your level.

Passing 3000 ft, G-IK.

G-IK, Report passing FL80.

Wilco, G-IK.

Then, when actually passing FL 80.

G-IK, Passing FL80.

G-JM, Climb to FL50.

Leaving 2000 ft, Climbing to FL50, G-JM.

G-CD, Request descent.

G-CD, Descend to FL40.

Leaving FL90, Descending to FL40, G-CD.

Oxbow 345, After passing North Cross descend to FL80.

After passing North Cross, Descend to FL80, Oxbow 345.

Having given clearance to climb or descend, a further overriding instruction may be given to a pilot by an Air Traffic Control Unit (ATCU).

Oxbow 345, Stop descent at FL110.

Stop descent at FL110, Oxbow 345.

Oxbow 348, Continue climb to FL150.

Climbing to FL150, Oxbow 348.

Oxbow 342, Recleared* FL170.

Recleared* FL170, Oxbow 342.

(*Note: "Recleared" is not used in the United Kingdom.)

Occasionally, for traffic reasons, a higher than normal rate of climb or descent may be required:

G-FHJM, Expedite descent to FL40.

Expediting descent to FL40, G-FHJM.

Oxbow 345, Climb to FL180, Expedite until passing FL75.

Climbing to FL80, Expediting until passing FL75, Oxbow 345.

It may not be possible for a pilot to comply with instructions to expedite a climb or descent because of aircraft performance limitations or other factors, in which case the response to such a request would be 'Unable', followed by the reason.

Oxbow 342, Expedite climb to FL200.

Unable to climb to FL200 due weight, Oxbow 342.

FLIGHT PLANS.

A pilot may file a flight plan with an Air Traffic Service Unit, during flight, over the radio. Pilots should, however, avoid using busy air traffic frequencies for this purpose. An appropriate frequency to use would be the Flight Information Service (FIS) frequency of the Flight Information Region (FIR), in which the pilot is flying. Details should be passed using the abbreviated flight plan format.

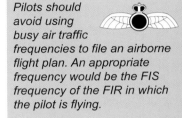

Pilots should avoid using busy air traffic frequencies to file an airborne flight plan. An appropriate frequency would be the FIS frequency of the FIR in which the pilot is flying.

Alexander Information, G-FHJM, Request file flight plan.

G-JM, Alexander Information, Ready to copy.

G-JM, PA-28, 10 miles South East of Kennington, Heading 320, Flight Level 45, VFR, Snodsbury to Stephenville, ETA Stephenville 1650, IAS 110 knots.

During a flight, a pilot may cancel an IFR flight if he wishes to continue the flight under VFR.

Alexander Control, G-EGIK, Cancelling IFR flight plan, Proceeding VFR, Estimating Stephenville at 17.

G-IK, IFR Flight plan cancelled at 47, Contact Alexander Information, 125.750.

When a pilot has expressed the intention of changing from IFR to VFR, the Air Traffic Service Unit should pass to the pilot any information which makes it likely that the flight will not be able to maintain VMC.

G-IK, IMC reported in the vicinity of Kennington.

Roger, Maintaining IFR, G-IK.

POSITION REPORTING.

When passing an RT position report to an Air Traffic Services Unit, a pilot should transmit a message containing the following elements of information:

The correct order and content of an aircraft Position Report are as follows:
- *Call sign*
- *Position*
- *Time*
- *Level or altitude*
- *Next position with ETA.*

1.   Aircraft identification.

2.   Position.

3.   Time.

4.   Level or altitude.

5.   Next position and estimated time of arrival (ETA) at that position.

Position reporting is more a feature of IFR flight than VFR flight, but it is, nevertheless, important that a VFR pilot should know how to pass a position report correctly.

G-JM, Daventry, 35, Flight Level 45, Cranfield 47.

G-JM, Roger.

CHAPTER 4
AERODROME CONTROL

INTRODUCTION.

The United Kingdom Civil Aviation Authority uses the following words to define an **aerodrome**:

"any area of land or water designed, equipped, set apart or commonly used for affording facilities for the landing and departure of aircraft...."

Figure 4.1 Oxford-Kidlington Aerodrome.

Aerodromes and airfields come in many shapes and sizes, of course; they range from large aerodromes or airports, which handle jet airliners, to small, grass landing strips.

The type of Air Traffic Service Unit (ATSU) established at an aerodrome will, generally, depend upon the number and frequency of take-offs and landings, often referred to as aircraft movements.

The three categories of aeronautical communication service provided to pilots which, in the case of VFR pilots, generally, but not exclusively, are provided by aerodrome ATSUs are:

1.   Full Air Traffic Control Service.

2.   Flight Information Service (also available on a Flight Information Region's FIS frequency.)

3.   Air-Ground Communications Service.

There are 3 categories of aeronautical communications service:
- *Full air traffic control.*
- *Flight Information Service.*
- *Air-Ground Communications service.*

Aerodromes with a Full Air Traffic Control Service.

The larger aerodromes are located near the centre of an area of controlled airspace known as a Control Zone (CTR), in which all air traffic movements are under the supervision and control of qualified air traffic controllers. Full air traffic control is exercised by an Air Traffic Control Unit, (ATCU). ATCUs operate on frequencies identified by the words GROUND and TOWER and are responsible for the control of

Pilots flying in, or transiting, an aerodrome with a CTR will be under air traffic control exercised by an ATCU.

aircraft flying in the aerodrome circuit, and taxying on the manoeuvring area, as well as of those aircraft flying in the immediate vicinity of the aerodrome circuit.

Aerodromes with a CTR will also invariably exercise approach control over aircraft approaching the CTR from outside its boundaries, or aircraft having just departed from the CTR. Approach Control is identified by the call-sign APPROACH. (See Chapter 5.) Sometimes approach control exists alongside zone and radar control.

ATCUs in CTRs usually, but not always, have separate TOWER, APPROACH, and RADAR frequencies.

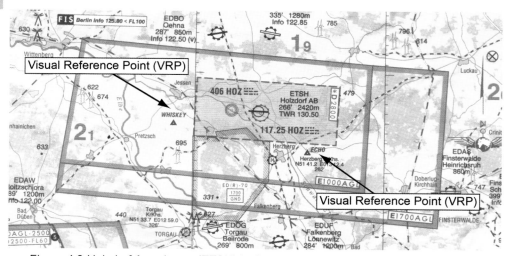

Figure 4.2 Holzdorf Aerodrome (ETSH) in Germany has a Class D CTR and an ATCU providing a full air traffic control service. Note the aerodrome frequency TOWER (TWR) of 130.5. When operating at an aerodrome with an ATCU, the pilot of an aircraft will conduct his movements on the ground and in the air under the control of that ATCU. WHISKEY and ECHO are VRPs.

Figure 4.2 depicts the aerodrome of Holzdorf, in Germany, which has a Class D CTR. The fact that Holzdorf has an ATCU is revealed by the designation of its aerodrome frequency of 130.5 as TOWER (TWR). WHISKEY and ECHO are Visual Reference Points (VRPs).

Figure 4.3 depicts Bristol aerodrome, in England. Its frequency of 125.650 is not identified as TOWER, but the fact that Bristol has a Class D CTR confirms that the aerodrome also has an ATCU, providing full air traffic control. The Bristol frequency is also identified as providing a Lower Airspace Radar Service (LARS), another indication that the ATSU at Bristol is a full ATCU. Visual Reference Points, relative to which arriving and departing aircraft report their position, are marked by the letter VRP.

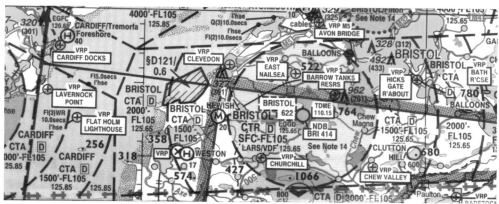

Fig 4.3 Aerodrome Flight Information Service.

Air Traffic Services Provided by Aerodromes with Aerodrome Traffic Zones.

Many smaller aerodromes, though, do not lie in controlled airspace, in which case, they do not have a CTR but are surrounded by an Aerodrome Traffic Zone (ATZ), established to protect aircraft flying in the aerodrome circuit.

Rules are established by national aviation authorities governing the operation of aircraft within an ATZ. Permission is required to operate within an ATZ. An aircraft must not take off, land or operate within the ATZ unless the Pilot-in-Command of the aircraft has obtained the permission of the responsible Air Traffic Service Unit (ATSU) to do so, irrespective of whether that ATSU is a full ATCU, providing full air traffic control, or a lower level of service.

Aerodromes within ATZs may operate a full air traffic control service from an ATCU, or a lower level of service such as an Aerodrome Flight Information Service (AFIS) or an Air-Ground Communication Service (AGCS). An AFIS does not exercise control of aircraft in the air, but gives information to pilots useful for the safe and efficient conduct of flights in the ATZ.

The key identifying aerodromes possessing an ATZ, on the 1: 500 000 aeronautical chart of Southern England and Wales, informs the pilot that Oxford Kidlington has an ATCU, while Northampton/Sywell provides an AFIS, and Haverfordwest has only an Air/Ground Communications Service. (*See Figures 4.4, 4.5 and 4.6.*)

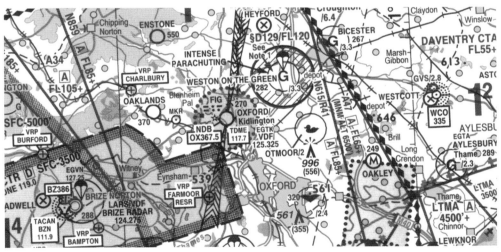

Figure 4.4 Oxford Kidlington has an ATZ and provides a full air traffic control service from an ATCU.

Figure 4.5 Northampton Sywell has an ATZ and provides an Aerodrome Flight Information Service.

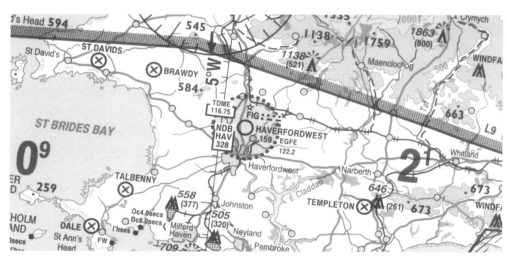

Figure 4.6 Haverfordwest has an ATZ provides an AIr/Ground Communications Service.

Aerodrome Flight Information Service.

When receiving an Aerodrome Flight Information Service (AFIS) from an aerodrome, a pilot is not under air traffic control while he is airborne. It is the responsibility of the Pilot-in-Command to decide the appropriate course of action to be taken to ensure the safe conduct of his flight and the safety of his aircraft when taking off, landing or flying in an ATZ which provides an AFIS. An AFIS-provider may not issue instructions or clearances to pilots.

A ground radio station operator providing an AFIS passes information only to aircraft which are flying in the ATZ, or about to enter the ATZ, though he may issue instructions to aircraft once they are on the ground.

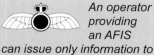

An operator providing an AFIS can issue only information to aircraft in flight, though he may issue instructions to aircraft on the ground.

An aerodrome at which an AFIS is provided will use the call-sign "INFORMATION", after the aerodrome identifier.

Figure 4.7 depicts the aerodrome of Magdeburg (EDBM) in Germany. Magdeburg is surrounded by a rectangular ATZ which is Class F airspace and, therefore, not controlled airspace. Magdeburg, then, does not have full air traffic control but an Airfield Flight Information Service (AFIS). This fact is confirmed by the appearance of the indicator INFO next to the aerodrome frequency of 119.30.

Figure 4.7 Magdeburg aerodrome has a Class F ATZ. The fact that Magdeburg provides an Aerodrome Flight Information Service is indicated by the word INFO next to the aerodrome frequency.

Air/Ground Communication Service.

However, some aerodromes which have an ATZ operate neither a full air traffic control service nor an Aerodrome Flight Information Service (AFIS). Airfields from which light aircraft operate often provide only an Air/Ground Communication Service (AGCS).

An AGCS will use the suffix "RADIO" following the name of the airfield.

An AGCS facility permits two way communication between an aircraft and a ground station, but the ground radio operator may pass only basic information regarding the situation at the aerodrome. An AGCS operator is not authorised to give any instructions to aircraft either in the air or on the ground. Pilots must, therefore, not ask an AGCS operator for instructions.

An AGCS is the simplest form of aeronautical radio communication service. Pilots using an AGCS must bear in mind that the AGCS station may even be located in a building that does not have an unrestricted view of the aerodrome.

An Air-Ground Communications Service provides only very basic information on the situation at an aerodrome. An ACGS operator is not authorised to give instructions to aircraft, either in the air or on the ground.

Figure 4.8 An Air/Ground Radio Communications Service may pass only very basic information regarding the situation at the aerodrome.

Qualifications of Operators of Ground Stations, and Permitted RT Phraseology.

The personnel who provide either a full Air Traffic Control Service, an Aerodrome Flight Information Service or an Air/Ground Communications Service hold very different qualifications.

The Air Traffic Controller is the most highly qualified individual and bears a heavy responsibility for the safely and expeditious operation for the aircraft under his control. An operator providing an Aerodrome Flight Information Service has a much lower level of qualification than an Air Traffic Controller, but is nevertheless licensed by the national aviation authority responsible for the aerodrome and airspace, in question. The Air-Ground Communications Operator is the lowest qualified of all; he is licensed operator of a ground radio installation who holds a Radio Operator's Certificate of Competence, but who has received no training for the national aviation authority.

The RT phraseology which Air Traffic Controllers, Flight Information Service Officers and Air Ground Communication Service Operators are authorised to use in the exercise of their responsibilities differs to reflect the different competencies of each office-holder.

The phraseology used by Flight Information Service Officers and Air Ground Communication Service Operators will be dealt with in the section of this book dealing with RT Communications in the United Kingdom.

This chapter deals with phraseologies used at an aerodrome with a full air traffic control service exercised by an ATCU. The speech patterns used by ATCU tend to be the same for all countries.

THE AIR TRAFFIC CONTROL UNIT AND AERODROME CONTROL.

Many light aircraft pilots operate exclusively from small airfields and may find the prospect of visiting aerodromes within a CTR intimidating; but it would be a pity if any pilot were to be discouraged from landing at a major aerodrome or airport because of lack of familiarly with the correct RT phraseology.

All pilots must know the full vocabulary used for RT communications, simply because when communicating with an ATSU they are likely to be exposed to every aspect of the language of RT, and must be able to understand the radio calls they receive, and to reply to ATCU transmissions appropriately.

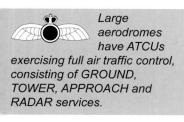

Large aerodromes have ATCUs exercising full air traffic control, consisting of GROUND, TOWER, APPROACH and RADAR services.

As we stated at the beginning of this chapter, Aerodrome Control at a large aerodrome, within a CTR or ATZ, is, typically, divided into the following services: GROUND, TOWER and APPROACH (and/or RADAR). Each service is normally contacted on its own frequency and has a call-sign composed of the name of the aerodrome plus the suffix, GROUND, TOWER, APPROACH or RADAR, respectively. Sometimes, when the aerodrome is not busy, Ground and Tower services may be provided by the same controller, as may Approach and Radar services.

The Ground Controller and Ground Movements.

Ground Movement Control provides services for a) aircraft moving on the apron b) aircraft and vehicles, obstructions and other aircraft on the manoeuvring area except on active runways and their access points.

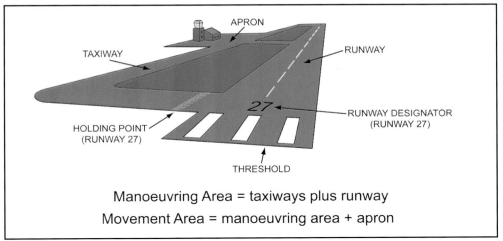

Figure 4.9 The principal elements of an aerodrome.

Initial calls from aircraft departing from the aerodrome, including requests for taxi clearance, and, at some aerodromes, start clearance, are made on the GROUND frequency. The pilot of a departing aircraft will normally remain on the GROUND frequency until he reaches the holding point of the runway-in-use.

Before first contact with GROUND, a pilot should select the Automatic Terminal Information Service (ATIS) frequency in order to obtain the latest weather and aerodrome information, including runway-in-use, wind and QNH. ATIS information is broadcast continuously and updated at least hourly. By listening out on the ATIS frequency before contacting GROUND, pilots can help ease the workload of controllers. ATIS information is identified by a letter of the alphabet (e.g. Mike, November etc), in order that controllers may know immediately whether or not a pilot is reporting having obtained the latest information. When departing, the pilot advises the GROUND controller, on his initial call, which ATIS information he is in possession of.

ATIS, the Automatic Terminal Information Service, continually transmits automated broadcasts containing aerodrome and weather information.

The content of an ATIS broadcast is typically along the lines of the following message:

This is Steerton Information Mike, timed at 1420Z. Runway 23, right hand circuit. Surface wind 260°, 10 kts, 10 kilometres in haze. Cloud broken at 2 500 ft. Outside air temperature +7°, dewpoint +6°, QNH 1015 hectopascal. On initial contact with Air Traffic Control, confirm the QNH and information Mike received.

When no ATIS is provided, a pilot may be able to obtain operational information directly from the ground frequency before start up.

Departure Information.

Steerton Ground, G-FHJM, VFR to Burfield, Request Departure information.

G-JM, Runway 32, Wind 290°, 8 knots, QNH 1015, Temperature 19.

Runway 32, QNH 1015, G-JM.

Notice that the pilot is required to readback only the runway-in-use and the QNH, as these are items essential to the safety of the flight, and the controller must be certain that the pilot has correctly understood the information.

Engine Starting Procedures.

At certain aerodromes with a high intensity of aircraft operations, aircraft may be required to request engine start in order to facilitate ATC planning. At certain aerodromes, along with the request, the pilot will state the location of the aircraft and acknowledge receipt of the departure ATIS broadcast identifying letter together with the QNH.

Steerton Ground, G-ABCD, Light Aircraft Park, Request start up, Information Mike, QNH 1002.

G-ABCD, Steerton Ground, Start up approved.

Start up approved, G-ABCD.

When there is a delay to the departure of the aircraft, the controller will normally indicate a time to start up or expect to start up.

Taxi Instructions.

When replying to a pilot's request for taxi instructions, a controller will include a clearance limit, which is the point at which the aircraft must stop until further permission to proceed is given. For departing aircraft, the clearance limit will normally be the holding point of the runway-in-use.

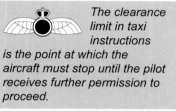

The clearance limit in taxi instructions is the point at which the aircraft must stop until the pilot receives further permission to proceed.

When issuing taxi instructions, the clearance limit imposed by the air traffic controller will normally, but not necessarily, be the holding point of the runway-in-use.

Steerton Ground, G-ABCD, Cessna 172, At the light aircraft parking area, Request taxi for VFR local flight, Information Mike.

G-ABCD, Taxi for Runway 23 via Taxiway Charlie to Holding Point Delta 1, Call approaching Holding Point Charlie, QNH 1010, Time 23.

Taxi for Runway 23 via Taxiway Charlie to Holding Point Delta 1, Wilco, QNH 1010, G-ABCD.

Note that if a pilot has reported receipt of the latest ATIS information, the controller will not normally pass departure information when issuing taxi instructions. The controller will, however, confirm that the pilot has the latest QNH.

Kennington Tower, G-FHJM, At the maintenance area, Request taxi to the flying club.

G-JM, Taxi via northwest taxiway to Holding Point Romeo, Runway 23.

Via northwest taxiway to Holding Point Romeo, Runway 23, G-JM.

G-JM, Holding Point Romeo, Runway 23.

G-JM, Hold short Runway 23.

> *A pilot must never cross a runway without permission, at an airfield with Air Traffic Control.*

Holding short, G-JM.

G-JM, Cross Runway 23, Report runway vacated, Continue to flying club.

CHAPTER 4: AERODROME CONTROL

When the aircraft has left the runway, the pilot reports "Runway vacated."

Crossing Runway 23, G-JM.

G-JM, Runway 23 Vacated.

G-JM, Roger.

Georgetown Ground, Oxbow 345, Request Taxi, Information Charlie.

Oxbow 345, Taxi for Runway 05 via Taxiway Juliet, Report at Holding Point Hotel Papa, Give way to 747 passing left to right, QNH 1019.

Holding point Hotel Papa, Via Taxiway Juliet, QNH 1019, Traffic in sight, Oxbow 345.

The Tower Controller.
Take-Off.

The TOWER controller is responsible for all traffic using the runway and all aircraft flying in the proximity to the aerodrome, including the circuit. Normally, an aircraft will be instructed to change to TOWER at, or approaching, the holding point of the runway-in-use.

G-CD, Contact Tower, 119.125.

Tower, 119.125, G-CD.

58

Steerton Tower, G-ABCD, Holding Point, Runway 27.

G-CD, Report when ready for departure.

Unless acknowledging a clearance to take-off the pilot should use the word 'Departure'.

Wilco, G-CD.

When a pilot is ready to take off, the correct words to transmit over the RT are: READY FOR DEPARTURE.

G-CD, Ready for departure.

G-CD, Line up Runway 27.

Lining up, Runway 27, G-CD.

G-CD, Cleared for take off, Runway 27.

Cleared for take off, Runway 27, G-CD.

At a busy aerodrome, it may be necessary for the aircraft to take off immediately after lining up.

G-IK, Are you ready for immediate departure?

Affirm, G-IK.

Having confirmed that he is ready for an immediate departure, the pilot must be able to comply with the take-off clearance, when it is given.

G-IK, cleared for immediate take-off, Runway 27.

Cleared for immediate take-off, Runway 27, G-IK.

If the aircraft is still at the holding point when cleared for immediate take-off, the pilot must line up immediately on the runway, and commence the take-off without stopping the aircraft. If he is already lined up, he must take-off without delay.

The Conditional Clearance.

A conditional clearance will normally be given only when all aircraft and/or vehicles included in the clearance can be seen by the controller issuing, and the pilot receiving, the clearance, and provided that the conditional clearance relates to one, single movement.

A conditional clearance is one where a condition must be met before the clearance may be acted upon. A conditional clearance will not normally be used except when the subject of the condition (e.g. an aircraft on short final) can be seen by both the controller and the pilot. When the conditional clearance involves a departing aircraft and an arriving aircraft, it is important that the departing aircraft correctly identifies the arriving aircraft on which the conditional clearance is based.

The arriving aircraft must be the first aircraft in the landing order on the approach.

A conditional clearance may apply to one single movement only. A conditional clearance will be given as follows:

- Call-sign of aircraft.

- The condition.

- The clearance.

- The condition, repeated.

G-IK, Report the Airbus on final in sight.

Airbus in sight, G-IK.

Figure 4.10 Airbus in sight.

G-IK, Behind the landing airbus, Line up and wait, Behind.

Behind the airbus, Line up and wait, Behind, G-IK.

Note: *In the United Kingdom, the condition is not repeated. In the United Kingdom, the clearance would be provided as follows: G-IK, Behind the landing Airbus, Line up and wait.*

Departure Instructions with Take-Off Clearance.

Local departure instructions may be given with the take-off clearance. The purpose of these instructions is normally to ensure separation between aircraft.

OXBOW 345, Climb straight ahead to 2 500 feet before turning right, Cleared for take off, Runway 02.

Climb straight ahead to 2 500 feet before turning right, Cleared for take off, Runway 02, OXBOW 345.

Unexpected developments, in air traffic movements may require a take-off to be cancelled or a runway to be vacated.

G-JM, Take off immediately or hold short of Runway 26.

Holding short, G-JM.

G-JM, Take off immediately or vacate runway 26.

Taking off, Runway 26, G-JM.

G-JM, Hold position, Cancel take off, I say again, Cancel take-off, Vehicle on Runway 26.

Holding, G-JM.

Should the controller require the aircraft to abandon the take-off after the aircraft has begun the take-off roll, the pilot will be instructed to stop immediately.

G-IK, Stop immediately, G-IK, Stop immediately.

Stopping, G-IK.

If it is the pilot who decides to abandon the take-off, he must announce this fact immediately and request assistance or taxi instructions.

OXBOW 345, Stopping.

OXBOW 345, Roger.

Request return to ramp, OXBOW 345.

OXBOW 345, Take next left, Return to ramp, Contact Ground 123.725.

Joining the Traffic Circuit.

The ATCU of an aerodrome which has a CTR will normally have separate approach and tower frequencies. Requests to join an aerodrome circuit pattern, must be made early enough for the ATCU to be able to plan to integrate the arriving aircraft into the traffic circuit, taking into account other aerodrome traffic. Arriving aircraft are handled first by the approach controller on the approach frequency, and then handed over to the tower controller on a distinct tower frequency. The hand-over will often take place immediately after the arriving aircraft reports its position in relation to a Visual Reference Point (VRP). VRPs are illustrated in *Figures 4.2* and *4.3*.

Chapter 5 deals with approach control. Here we will consider the arriving aircraft after it has changed from the approach to the tower frequency, and is inside the CTR.

The standard circuit pattern is a left hand pattern as illustrated in *Figure 4.11*. If a right hand circuit pattern is in force, this will be stipulated by the tower controller.

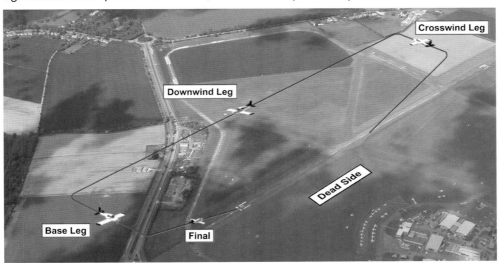

Figure 4.11 A left-hand circuit pattern.

The following exchange of RT transmissions between the **control tower** and an arriving aircraft take place after the aircraft has been handed over to **TOWER** near the **Visual Reference Point (VRP)** of **Hartlade**. (*See Figure 4.12.*)

If in doubt about the circuit direction, confirm with ATC.

Steerton Tower, G-ABCD, Hartlade, 1 500 feet, QNH 1011.

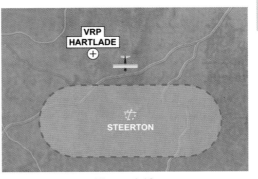

Figure 4.12.

Note that only the basic details of **G-ABCD's** position are given by its pilot during the initial call to **TOWER**. This is because the aircraft has been handed over to **TOWER** from **APPROACH**, and the **tower controller** will, therefore, know **G-ABCD's** position and intentions. However, the pilot might justifiably wish to add the information **'for landing'**.

G-CD, Join left hand downwind, Runway 02 , wind 030°, 5 knots, QNH 1012, Report downwind.

Join left hand downwind, Runway 02, QNH 1012, Wilco, G-CD.

At airfields where an Automatic Terminal Information Service (ATIS) is provided, receipt of the broadcast may be re-confirmed in the initial call to TOWER.

Steerton Tower, G-FHJM, Hartlade, 1 500 feet, QNH 998, Information Bravo.

G-JM, Join right base for Runway 02, Right Hand, QNH 996, Report right base.

Join right base, Runway 20, Right Hand, QNH 996 Wilco, G-JM.

Required position reports whilst flying in the circuit are 'Downwind' and 'Final.' Additional position reports are made as and when instructed.

 G-CD, Downwind, Runway 02.

 G-CD, Number 2, follow the Warrior on Base, Report Base.

 Number 2, Traffic in sight, Wilco, G-CD.

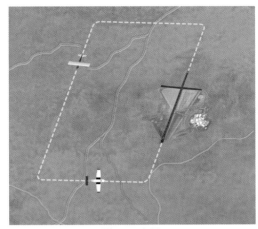

Figure 4.13.

 G-CD, Base leg.

 G-CD, Report Final.

 Wilco, G-CD.

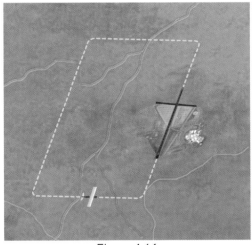

Figure 4.14.

 G-CD, Final, Runway 20.

 G-CD, Continue approach, Wind 200°, 7 knots.

 Continue, G-CD.

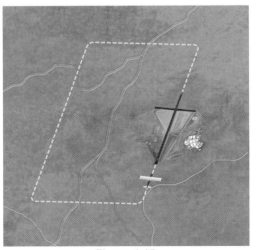

Figure 4.15.

When there are several aircraft in the circuit, it may be necessary for the tower controller to issue delaying or expediting instructions to individual aircraft.

G-CD, Downwind, Runway 20.

G-CD, Extend downwind, Number 2, Follow Warrior, 2 miles final.

Wilco, Number 2, Warrior in sight, G-CD.

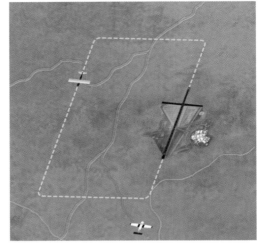

Figure 4.16.

G-CD, Downwind, Runway 20.

G-CD, Make one orbit right, Warrior 2 miles final, Report left base.

Orbiting Right, Wilco, G-CD.

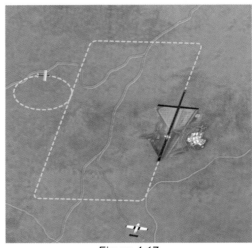

Figure 4.17.

G-CD, Downwind, Runway 20.

G-CD, Number 1, Make short approach, Warrior 6 miles final.

Number 1, Wilco G-CD.

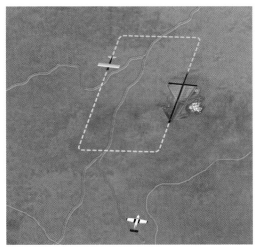

Figure 4.18.

Final Approach and Landing.

A pilot reports FINAL when he turns from base leg onto final approach, in the runway direction.

If a straight-in approach has been approved, the report of "FINAL" may be given up to 4 nautical miles from the runway threshold. If an aircraft is required to, or needs to, report FINAL further out than 4 miles, the words LONG FINAL should be used.

Note that the word used to report final is FINAL and not ~~FINALS~~.

A FINAL report is made when the aircraft is approaching the runway, in the runway direction, within 4 nautical miles of the runway threshold.

G-JM, Final, Runway 20.

G-JM, Runway 20, Cleared to land, Wind 230°, 5 knots.

Runway 20, Cleared to land, G-JM.

G-IK, Long final, Runway 06.

 G-IK, Continue approach, Wind 050°, 8 knots.

 Continue, G-IK.

 G-IK, Final, Runway 06.

 G-IK, Cleared to land, Runway 06, wind 050°, 5 kts.

 Runway 06, Cleared to land, G-IK.

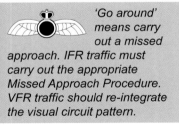

'Go around' means carry out a missed approach. IFR traffic must carry out the appropriate Missed Approach Procedure. VFR traffic should re-integrate the visual circuit pattern.

Missed Approach.

If, for any reason, the tower controller requires a pilot to carry out a missed approach, and not to land, the instruction GO AROUND will be given. If a pilot were flying in accordance with the Instrument Flight Rules, he would carry out the published missed approach procedure for the aerodrome in question. A pilot flying in accordance with the Visual Flight Rules, would re-integrate the visual circuit pattern.

 G-JM, Go around, Aircraft on runway.

 Going around, G-JM.

If it is the pilot who initiates the missed approach, he uses the words GOING AROUND.

 G-CD, Going around.

 G-CD, Roger, Report downwind.

 Wilco, G-CD.

Landing.

After touch-down, when the aircraft is fully under control, the pilot of a light aircraft will probably gently apply the brakes to slow the aircraft to a fast walking pace. The tower controller may then instruct the pilot to turn off the runway at the next appropriate exit. However, the tower controller may require the pilot to vacate the runway by any exit.

 G-IK, Vacate left.

 Vacate left, G-IK.

Pilots will normally be instructed to change to GROUND after vacating the runway.

 G-JM, Take second left, When vacated contact Ground, 118.35.

 Second left, Ground, 118.35, G-JM.

When the pilot has exited the runway, he reports RUNWAY VACATED. Under no circumstances must the word CLEAR be used.

Notice that, having exited the runway, the pilot reports "RUNWAY VACATED". Under no circumstances, should the word "CLEAR" be used.

Steerton Ground, G-FHJM, Runway vacated.

G-JM, Taxi to light aircraft parking area.

Wilco, G-JM.

CHAPTER 5
APPROACH CONTROL

APPROACH CONTROL.

This chapter deals only with the RT aspects of approaches to, and departures from, aerodromes which have an Air Traffic Control Unit (ATCU); that is, a Unit exercising full air traffic control over the aircraft with which it is in contact.

Furthermore, we will consider only the case of aircraft, under approach control, which are flying in accordance with the Visual Flight Rules (VFR).

Approach controllers normally carry out their functions in a part of the Air Traffic Control Tower from which they cannot see the outside world. Approach control may be either radar or non-radar.

At busy aerodromes a radar controller may operate alongside the approach controller to provide services for traffic transiting the area.

Figure 5.1 Approach Control.

An ATCU at an aerodrome within controlled airspace provides approach control services to all aircraft within its area of jurisdiction.

Arriving traffic is passed from approach control to aerodrome control, normally to the tower frequency.

Departing traffic is taken over by approach control, from the tower until the traffic has left the Control Zone (CTR). Approach control is usually also responsible for the control of aircraft transiting a CTR.

An ATCU providing an approach control service uses the call-sign APPROACH
or RADAR, as appropriate.

ARRIVING VFR TRAFFIC.

Non-controlled VFR flights approaching an aerodrome with an ATCU will contact APPROACH, and remain under approach control until control is transferred to TOWER.

You should note that, if the aerodrome to which you are flying provides a RADAR service, you may make initial contact with the RADAR frequency instead of the APPROACH frequency. The radar controller will then probably remain in communication with you until you are in visual contact with the aerodrome, at which point you will be instructed to contact TOWER. However, if there is no radar service, your initial call will be to APPROACH.

Figure 5.2 Approaching Oxford ATZ.

Arriving VFR aircraft will normally contact the APPROACH or RADAR frequency of their destination airfield, at about 15 nautical miles or 10 minutes from a zone boundary, either a CTR or an ATZ.

The joining procedure at an aerodrome can vary depending on local conditions, usually the local traffic situation or noise abatement issues. If IFR traffic is operating from the aerodrome, a pilot will not, with very few exceptions, be offered an overhead join. Most likely, arriving pilots will be instructed to report their position relative to a Visual Reference Point (VRP).

If the aerodrome you are approaching has an Aerodrome Terminal Information Service (ATIS) frequency, a pilot should note the ATIS information before initial contact with APPROACH. When the pilot contacts APPROACH, he should then inform the controller that he has noted the ATIS information. (See Chapter 11.) If no ATIS frequency is available, the approach controller will pass aerodrome information to the pilot.

If you have never visited an aerodrome before, or are otherwise unfamiliar with the aerodrome of destination, be prepared for your workload on arrival to be high. You may not recognise geographical features, or even recognise the airfield immediately it comes within visual range. You will need to plan your descent and carry out the accompanying checks, as well as report your position and change frequency. Therefore, plan your arrival thoroughly during your pre-flight planning. During the approach phase, itself, keep a good lookout for other traffic.

Steerton Approach, G-ABCD.

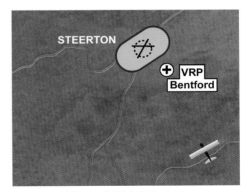

G-ABCD, Steerton Approach, Go Ahead.*

Figure 5.3 VFR Arrival.

G-ABCD, Cessna 172, VFR from Walden to Steerton, 2000 feet, Warbury QNH 1005**, Estimating zone boundary 47, Information Mike.

G-CD, Cleared to Steerton from control zone boundary, VFR, Not above 1300 feet, Steerton QNH 1004, Report Bentford with field in sight.⁺

Cleared from control zone boundary to Steerton, VFR, Not above 1300 feet, QNH 1004, Wilco, G-CD.

Some minutes later:

G-CD, Bentford, Field in sight.

G-CD, Contact Tower, 123.3.

Notes:

*   *In the United Kingdom, the words **"Pass your message"** are spoken instead of "Go Ahead".*

**   *In the United Kingdom, this pressure setting would be given as a **Regional Pressure Setting**, e.g. **"Cotswold 1007"**.*

⁺   *As the pilot has obtained the latest **ATIS** information, the approach controller will not need to give the pilot runway-in-use or wind information, but the controller will confirm the airfield **QNH**.*

Tower, 123.3, G-CD.

Steerton Tower, G-ABCD, Bentford, Field in sight, Information Mike.

Figure 5.4 Airfield in sight.

G-CD, Report right base, Runway 20, QNH 1004.

Wilco, Runway 20, QNH 1004, G-CD.

TRANSITING A CONTROL ZONE.

If a pilot flying cross-country wishes to transit an aerodrome's Control Zone (CTR), it is with the aerodrome's APPROACH frequency that he would make the transit request.

Most CTRs in the United Kingdom are Class D controlled airspace. This is not necessarily the case in other European countries, though Germany's CTRs are frequently Class D, too. VFR flight is permitted in Class D airspace, subject to clearance from Air Traffic Control, whereas in the case of a Class A CTR a Special VFR (SVFR) clearance would be required.

An example of a pilot's request for a CTR transit is given on the next page. Always bear in mind that the approach controller may make a judgment on the competence of a VFR pilot from the manner in which the pilot makes the transit request and subsequent RT transmissions. An RT transmission made up of the correct RT phraseology and content, which is delivered in a professional manner, will do much to persuade the approach controller of the pilot's competence, whereas a hesitant and poorly structured transmission will probably have the opposite effect and cause the controller to think twice about issuing the pilot a clearance to transit the CTR.

Steerton Approach, G-FHJM, Request zone transit.

G-FHJM, Steerton Approach, Go Ahead.*

G-FHJM, PA 28, Warbury to Netherton, VFR, 5 miles South of Barford, 2500 feet, On Warbury QNH 997, Estimate control zone boundary, 17, Request control zone transit.

G-FHJM, Cleared to enter the Steerton Control Zone abeam Croft, VFR, Not below 2000 feet, QNH 998, Report Croft.

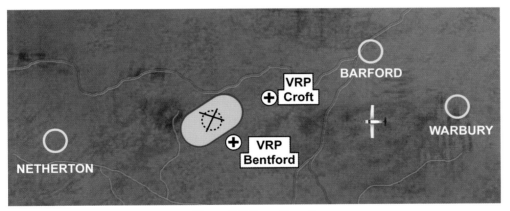

Figure 5.5 Zone Transit.

Cleared to enter the Steerton Control Zone abeam Croft, Not below 2000 feet, QNH 998, Wilco, G-JM.

Note:

* *In the UK: **"Pass your message"**.*

DEPARTING VFR TRAFFIC.

The pilot of a VFR flight leaving a CTR will normally be instructed by TOWER to contact APPROACH shortly after take-off. APPROACH will normally control a departing aircraft until the aircraft has left the CTR, and may pass the pilot information to assist him in maintaining separation from other traffic.

G-CD, Contact Approach, 132.5.

Approach, 132.5, G-CD.

Steerton Approach, G-ABCD.

G-CD, Report control zone boundary, Not above 1300 feet.

Not above 1300 feet, Wilco, G-CD.

Pilots should inform APPROACH when they have passed the CTR boundary.

G-CD, Passing the control zone boundary.

G-CD, Roger, Report leaving the frequency.

Wilco, G-CD.

SPECIAL VFR (SVFR).

Aircraft departing a control zone with a Special VFR (SVFR) clearance will be cleared to depart the zone in accordance with laid down procedures.

A SVFR Flight is a VFR flight cleared by an Air Traffic Control Unit (ATCU) to operate within a Control Zone (CTR) in meteorological conditions below VMC.

A Special VFR Clearance permits a VFR pilot to fly in a CTR when meteorological conditions are below VMC, and where, normally, an IFR clearance would be required.

The important points to remember about SVFR are:

- An SVFR clearance is granted by an ATCU only when traffic conditions allow, after a request has been made by the pilot.

- An SVFR flight must obey all instructions from the ATCU.

- An SVFR flight must remain clear of cloud and in sight of the ground at all times.

- An SVFR flight is allowed only within a CTR.

- Separation is provided between SVFR aircraft and all IFR traffic.

- Two-way communications are mandatory. It should be noted that if a pilot has received an SVFR clearance to enter a CTR and experiences a communications failure prior to entry, the pilot must remain clear of the CTR.

- A pilot may request SVFR in flight or prior to take-off from an aerodrome in the CTR.

A pilot is not required to submit a full flight plan to obtain an SVFR clearance to enter a CTR, but he must give brief details concerning this flight when requesting an SVFR clearance. For instance, if requesting an SVFR clearance, in flight, the pilot should pass the following details to the Air Traffic Control Unit with which he is in contact.

1. Call-sign.

2. Aircraft type.

3. The pilot's intentions.

4. The Estimated Time of Arrival at the **CTR** entry point.

CHAPTER 6
THE FLIGHT
INFORMATION SERVICE

WHAT IS A FLIGHT INFORMATION SERVICE?

A Flight Information Service (FIS) is an Air Traffic Service provided by Air Traffic Service Units (ATSU) and Flight Information Region (FIR) Centres to aircraft flying in uncontrolled airspace for the purpose of supplying information to pilots which is useful for the safe, orderly and efficient conduct of flights.

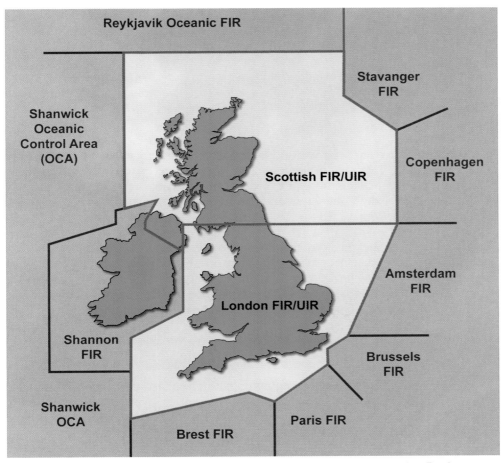

Figure 6.1 The lateral limits of the London and Scottish Flight Information Regions.

The FIS is probably the service most frequently used by VFR pilots who are on cross country flights in uncontrolled (Class G) airspace, sometimes known as the Open FIR. Of course, there is no reason why a pilot should not ask for an FIS from a convenient ATSU while on a <u>local</u> flight.

AIR TRAFFIC SERVICES OUTSIDE CONTROLLED AIRSPACE

The UK Flight Information Services (FIS) is a suite of services which includes air traffic units and air traffic control centres. These provide a Flight Information and Alerting Service in uncontrolled airspace within the UK FIR.

There are four distinct Flight Information Services. These are:
1.   Basic Service
2.   Traffic Service

3. Deconfliction Service
4. Procedural Service

Regardless of the service being provided, pilots are ultimately responsible for collision avoidance and terrain clearance, and they should consider service provision to be constrained by the unpredictable nature of this environment.

It is the pilot's responsibility to determine the appropriate service for the various phases and conditions of flight and request that service from the controller/FISO. An Alerting Service will be provided in association with all services.

Controllers will make all reasonable endeavours to provide the service that a pilot requests. However, controller workload or resources available may limit the service that can be offered.

Basic Service.

A Basic Service provides advice and information useful for the safe and efficient conduct of flights. This may include weather information, changes of serviceability of facilities, conditions at aerodromes, general airspace activity information, and any other information likely to affect safety. The avoidance of other traffic is solely the pilot's responsibility.

Pilots should not expect any form of traffic information from a controller/FISO and the pilot remains responsible for collision avoidance at all times. However, on initial contact the controller/FISO may provide traffic information in general terms to assist with the pilot's situational awareness. This will not normally be updated by the controller/FISO unless the situation changes markedly, or the pilot requests an update.

A Basic Service is available at all levels and the pilot remains responsible for terrain clearance at all times.

Unless the pilot has entered into an agreement with a controller to maintain a specific course of action, a pilot may change heading, route, or level without advising the controller. A controller will not issue specific heading instructions; however, generic navigational assistance may be provided on request.

Air Traffic Control Centres (ACC).

A Basic Service is also provided by ACCs (Callsign London Information and Scottish Information) through an FIS Officer (FISO) operating on specially allocated RTF channels.

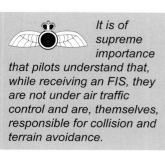

It is of supreme importance that pilots understand that, while receiving an FIS, they are not under air traffic control and are, themselves, responsible for collision and terrain avoidance.

In addition to the normal Basic Service described above, the FISO will:

(a) On receipt of a request for joining or crossing clearance of Controlled Airspace or Advisory Routes either:

(i) Inform the pilot that he should change frequency in time to make the request direct to the appropriate ATC Unit at least 10 minutes before ETA for the entry or crossing point or

(ii) Obtain the clearance from the appropriate ATC Unit himself and pass it to the pilot on the FIR frequency.

(b) Pass ETA to destination aerodromes in special circumstances, such as diversions, or at particular locations when traffic conditions demand it. Normally, however, pilots who wish destination aerodromes outside Controlled Airspace to have prior warning of arrival should communicate direct with ATC at the aerodrome concerned, at least 10 minutes before ETA.

(c) Accept airborne flight plans and pass the information to the appropriate authority.

The service from London Information will be provided by one controller only; pilots are therefore asked to keep their use of it to a minimum.

Due to the possibility of simultaneous aircraft transmissions, the response to RTF calls may be affected. Requests for joining or crossing airways within the London FIR should continue to be made on the London FIS frequencies rather than direct on the Controlled Airspace sector frequencies.

FISOs are not licensed to provide a Traffic Service, Deconfliction Service or Procedural Service

Traffic Service.

A Traffic Service is a surveillance based ATS, where in addition to the provisions of a Basic Service, the controller provides specific surveillance derived traffic information to assist the pilot in avoiding other traffic.

If a controller issues a heading and/or level that would require flight in IMC, a pilot who is not suitably qualified to fly in IMC shall inform the controller and request alternative instructions.

The controller will pass traffic information on relevant traffic, and update the traffic information if it continues to constitute a definite hazard, or if requested by the pilot. However, high controller workload and RTF loading may reduce the ability of the controller to pass traffic information, and the timeliness of such information. Whether traffic information has been passed or not, a pilot is expected to discharge his collision avoidance responsibility without assistance from the controller. If, after receiving traffic information, a pilot requires deconfliction advice, an upgrade to a Deconfliction Service shall be requested.

Subject to ATS surveillance system coverage, a Traffic Service may be provided at any level and the pilot remains responsible for terrain clearance at all times.

A pilot may operate under his own navigation or a controller may provide headings and levels for the purpose of positioning, sequencing or as navigational assistance. If a heading or level is unacceptable to the pilot, he shall advise the controller immediately. Unless safety is likely to be compromised, a pilot shall not change level, route, manoeuvring area, or deviate from an ATC heading without first advising and obtaining a response from the controller.

Deconfliction Service.

A Deconfliction Service is a surveillance based ATS where, in addition to the provisions of a Basic Service, the controller provides specific surveillance derived traffic information and deconfliction advice.

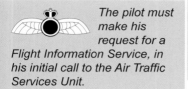 *The pilot must make his request for a Flight Information Service, in his initial call to the Air Traffic Services Unit.*

The controller will expect the pilot to accept headings and/or levels that may require flight in IMC. A pilot who is not suitably qualified to fly in IMC shall not request a Deconfliction Service unless compliance permits the flight to be continued in VMC. A controller will provide traffic information, accompanied with a heading and/or level aimed at achieving a planned deconfliction minima.

High controller workload or RTF loading may reduce the ability of the controller to pass such deconfliction advice; furthermore, unknown aircraft may make unpredictable or high-energy manoeuvres. Consequently, controllers cannot guarantee to achieve these deconfliction minima; however, they shall apply all reasonable endeavors. The avoidance of traffic is ultimately the pilot's responsibility.

The pilot shall inform the controller if he elects not to act on the controller's deconfliction advice, and therefore accepts responsibility for initiating any subsequent collision avoidance against that particular conflicting aircraft.

A Deconfliction Service will only be provided to aircraft operating at or above a terrain safe level, unless on departure from an aerodrome when climbing to a terrain safe level, or when following notified instrument approach procedures. If a controller detects a confliction when an aircraft is departing from an aerodrome and climbing to the terrain safe level, or when following notified instrument approach procedures, traffic information without deconfliction advice shall be passed. However, if the pilot requests deconfliction advice, or the controller considers that a definite risk of collision exists, the controller shall immediately offer such advice.

Unless safety is likely to be compromised, a pilot shall not change heading or level without first obtaining approval from the controller.

Procedural Service.
A Procedural Service is a non surveillance ATS where, in addition to the provisions of a Basic Service, the controller provides instructions which, if complied with, shall achieve deconfliction minima against other aircraft participating in the Procedural Service.

Neither traffic information nor deconfliction advice can be passed with respect to unknown traffic.

The controller will expect the pilot to accept levels, radials, tracks and time allocations that may require flight in IMC. A pilot who is not suitably qualified to fly in IMC shall not request a Procedural Service unless compliance permits the flight to be continued in VMC.

A Procedural Service is available at all levels and the pilot remains wholly responsible for terrain clearance at all times.

A controller will provide deconfliction instructions by allocating levels, radials, tracks, and time restrictions, or use pilot position reports, aimed at achieving a planned deconfliction minima. The pilot shall inform the controller if he elects not to act on the controller's deconfliction advice, and therefore accepts responsibility for initiating any subsequent collision avoidance against the aircraft in question and any other aircraft affected.

The controller will provide traffic information on conflicting aircraft being provided with a Basic Service and those where traffic information has been passed by another

ATS unit; however, there is no requirement for deconfliction advice to be passed, and the pilot is wholly responsible for collision avoidance.

Unless safety is likely to be compromised, a pilot shall not change level, radial, track, or time restriction without first obtaining approval from the controller.

If a level, radial, track, or time restriction is unacceptable to the pilot, he shall advise the controller immediately.

Reference to specific ATSUs can be found in the ENR section 6-1-10-1 of the AIP 22

RESPONSIBILITIES OF FIS PROVIDERS.

The list below illustrates the type of responsibility FIS providers have with respect to pilots who request an FIS:

- Provision of weather information including SIGMETs.

- Provision of information on changes of serviceability of navigational aids and other facilities at relevant aerodromes or air traffic control centres.

- Provision of information on changes of conditions at aerodromes, including information on the state of the aerodrome movement areas when they are affected by such things as repair work, snow, ice or significant depths of water.

- Provision of any other information pertinent to safety, including general traffic information.

- Provision of an alerting service.

- Initiating overdue action.

- Provision of collision hazard warnings.

- Provision of available information concerning traffic and weather conditions along the route of the flight that are likely to make operation under the Visual Flight Rules impracticable.

LIMITATIONS OF THE FLIGHT INFORMATION SERVICE.

N.B. There are numerous factors which limit the air traffic service given to a pilot receiving an FIS. For instance, because aerodromes and centres providing an FIS need only be equipped to a specified minimum level, accurate assessment of the possibility of collision hazard between aircraft in flight is low. It is, therefore, recognised that no form of positive control or separation service can be provided to pilots receiving an FIS. Indeed, as we write above, it is of supreme importance that pilots understand that, while receiving an FIS, they are not under air traffic control and are, themselves, responsible for collision and terrain avoidance.

A VFR PILOT'S RESPONSIBILITIES WHEN RECEIVING A FLIGHT INFORMATION SERVICE.

In any exchange of radio transmissions between a pilot and an ATSU, the pilot bears the general responsibility for transmitting his intentions, requests and responses succinctly, clearly and effectively to the ground operator. Professional pilots are specifically trained in radio communication techniques, but the typical private pilot, flying VFR, will not have received such training. It is, therefore, incumbent on the VFR pilot wishing to become an effective user of airspace and of air traffic control services to take responsibility for his own training and skill-development in this field.

Of one thing you may be certain: if you are to gain maximum benefit from the services that ATSUs can provide you, as a VFR pilot, the manner in which you use your radio must make it clear to the ATSU operator that you are a competent and proficient pilot, navigator and radio operator.

Being aware of your responsibilities in this field will help you attain that level of proficiency. Here is a list of some of the responsibilities of a VFR pilot when receiving a Flight Information Service.

- Prepare each flight thoroughly.

- Keep an attentive listening watch on the FIS frequency you are working.

- Maintain good radio discipline.

- Learn how to pass your position messages in a professional manner.

- When transmitting, use standard operating procedures and RT speech groups.

- Make your radio transmissions as succinct as possible to avoid congesting the frequency.

- Always report leaving an FIS frequency to avoid any uncertainty arising in the mind of the FIS provider about your whereabouts and/or safety.

- Remember that receiving an FIS does not free you from your obligation to plan your flight thoroughly.

- Always be aware of your present location and be prepared to report your position whenever you are asked to do so by the FIS provider.

- Finally always remember that you are not under air traffic control and that you remain responsible at all times for avoiding collision.

THE REPLY TO "GO AHEAD" ("PASS YOUR MESSAGE" IN THE UNITED KINGDOM.)

When you contact an ATSU to request a Flight Information Service, your transmission will take the following form. Note that the request for the Flight Information Service is made after the initial call.

"Stephenville Approach, G-ABCD, Request Flight Information Service"

The Controller will reply:

"G-ABCD, Stephenville Approach, Go Ahead"

(NB: In the United Kingdom, the controller will reply: "G-ABCD, Stephenville Approach, Pass your message.")

Your response, as a pilot, to the instruction "Go Ahead" ("Pass Your Message") will be to pass a standard report combining details of your aircraft type, position, altitude, route and intentions. A typical pilot response to the "Go Ahead" ("Pass Your Message") instruction would be:

"G-ABCD, PA-28, From Rissington Parva to Georgetown, 15 miles East of Stephenville, 2500 feet, QNH 987, VFR, Estimate Wicken, 46."

You will notice that the pilot has passed his details in the order:

- Aircraft call-sign. **G-ABCD.**

- Aircraft type. **PA-28.**

- Departure Point and Destination. **From Rissington Parva to Georgetown.**

- Present Position. **15 miles East of Stephenville.**

- Altitude or Level. **2 500 feet, QNH 987*.**

- Additional details and Intentions (e.g. Flight Rules, Next point on route.) **VFR, Estimate Wicken 46.**

*_N.B. In the **United Kingdom**, instead of an airfield **QNH**, a pilot flying a cross-country route would probably pass the **Regional Pressure Setting** that he has set on the altimeter subscale. For example:_ **"Cotswold 990".**

A reply composed in the above way will help the ATC controller to visualize your details, and, thus, to give you a better service. By passing your details clearly and crisply, you will also do a lot to convince the controller that he is dealing with a competent pilot/radio operator.

LONDON FLIGHT INFORMATION SERVICE - INTRODUCTION OF SSR CODE 7401. (UNITED KINGDOM ONLY)

The volume of air traffic around the world's major cities has increased tremendously in recent years, particularly in the United Kingdom, in the London area. From 23 November 2006, in order to prevent and mitigate the consequences of controlled airspace incursions inside the London FIR, all pilots requesting an FIS from London FIS will be requested to "squawk" SSR Code 7401. This will enable radar equipped ATSUs in the London FIR, which observe aircraft displaying this code, following tracks which could infringe their airspace, to contact London FIS and ask for the flight details of the aircraft concerned. ATSUs will also request that the aircraft be advised to contact them so that they may resolve the situation as expeditiously as possible.

This procedure in no way implies that London FIS is providing a radar service. The London FIS will continue to provide a Flight Information Service only. Pilots who contact London FIS making short-duration calls, e.g. for weather reports, and are in contact with London FIS for only short periods of time, will not be required to squawk 7401.

CHAPTER 7
GENERAL RADAR
PHRASEOLOGY

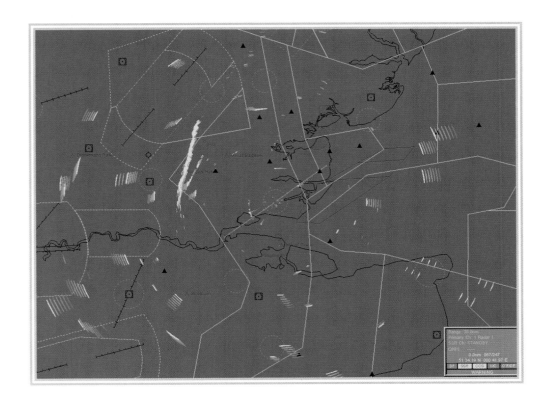

RADAR PHRASEOLOGY.

This chapter will deal with general radar phraseology which is commonly used in communications between aircraft and all types of radar unit.

Phraseology applicable to radar services available to general aviation pilots, in the United Kingdom only, within the context of the United Kingdom's Lower Airspace Radar Service (LARS) is dealt with in the United Kingdom Airspace Section of this volume.

You should note that the phrase 'under radar control' is used by air traffic controllers <u>only</u> when a radar control service is being provided. General aviation pilots who do not hold an Instrument Rating are unlikely to find themselves under radar control.

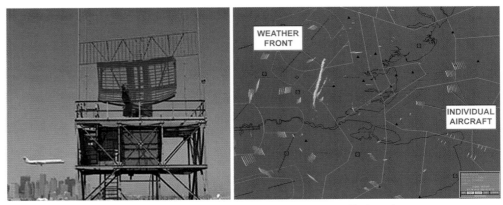

Figure 7.1 A radar head, and radar returns on a controller's radar screen.
(Photo of radar screen display by kind permission of London Southend Airport Co Ltd.).

If a pilot qualified for flight in Visual Meteorological Conditions (VMC) only is given instructions by a radar controller, in the form of headings to be steered and level changes, the pilot must inform the radar controller immediately if an instruction to alter heading or height makes it impossible for the pilot to maintain VMC at all times.

RADAR IDENTIFICATION.

Before any radar service can be provided to a pilot, for instance, if a pilot requires to confirm his position, the aircraft must be identified by the radar controller. Identification is often achieved by the radar controller giving the pilot a radar vector, that is, a heading to steer. The issuing of radar vectors does not, however, in itself, constitute a radar service.

If a radar service has been requested, the radar controller will confirm that a radar service is being provided, if he is able to comply with the request. In the following example, the exchange between the radar controller and pilot illustrates an identification procedure only.

G-IK, Report your heading and level.

Heading 110 at 2500 feet, G-IK.

G-IK, For identification, Turn left heading 080.

Left heading 080, G-IK.

G-IK, Identified, Position is 10 miles North of Steerton, Resume own navigation.

Wilco, G-IK.

Notice that when a radar instruction has been carried out to the satisfaction of the controller, the radar controller instructs the pilot to "resume your own navigation."

Other means of radar identification are:

- Position report information from the pilot to the radar controller.

- Secondary Surveillance Radar.

RT phraseology to be used in conjunction with Secondary Surveillance Radar is covered later in this chapter.

LOSS OF RADAR IDENTIFICATION.

Whenever a pilot is receiving a radar service he must always bear in mind that radar can fail. An aircraft may be too far away from, or too close to, the radar head, or too low to be detected by the radar controller. But if radar contact is lost, or about to be lost, the controller will always inform the pilot of that fact, and will pass on instructions appropriate to the situation.

The following transmissions are examples of the sorts of calls a pilot might hear when a radar controller can no longer maintain adequate radar contact with his aircraft.

G-IK, Not identified, Not yet within radar cover, Resume own navigation to Marlow.

Wilco, G-IK.

G-IK, Radar identification lost due radar failure, Contact Alexander Control on 128.750.

Roger, 128.750, G-IK.

G-IK, Will shortly lose radar identification as you are entering my radar overhead, Remain this frequency.

Wilco, G-IK.

TRAFFIC INFORMATION.

Whenever possible, information regarding traffic on a conflicting path will be given as detailed in *Figure 7.2*, below.

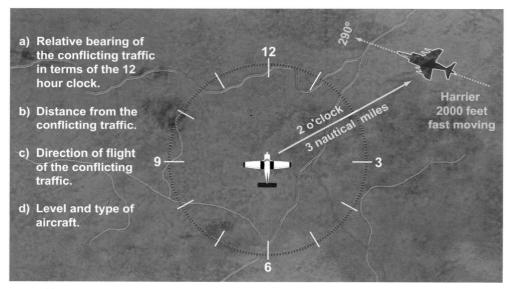

a) **Relative bearing of the conflicting traffic in terms of the 12 hour clock.**

b) **Distance from the conflicting traffic.**

c) **Direction of flight of the conflicting traffic.**

d) **Level and type of aircraft.**

Figure 7.2. Traffic information uses the 12-hour clock code to indicate direction.

Relative movements of traffic will be described by using the expressions in the list below, either singly or in a combination, in order to give the pilot as clear a picture as possible of the situation.

The terms are:

- ***Closing*** — The range of the contact aircraft is decreasing, with respect to the aircraft with which the radar controller is communicating. There is not necessarily a risk of collision.

- ***Converging*** — The contact is on a converging course. There is a risk of collision, and vectors should be requested if the contact is not seen.

- ***Overtaking*** — The contact is travelling faster than the aircraft receiving the radar service, in the same or similar direction.

- ***Crossing left to right / right to left.*** — The track of contact will cross in the direction indicated.

Figure 7.3. A fast moving contact.

The following examples illustrate the use of some of the terms defined on the previous page:

   G-JM, Unknown traffic, 1 o'clock, 3 miles, Closing, Fast moving.

   Looking, G-JM

   Traffic in sight, Now passed clear, G-JM.

If a contact is described as closing, it means that the contact's range from the aircraft receiving the traffic information is decreasing. The word closing does not necessarily mean that there is a collision risk.

Depending on the circumstances, if a pilot cannot see the contact aircraft, avoidance vectors may be offered by the radar controller or requested by the pilot.

If avoidance vectors have been given, the controller should inform the pilot when the conflict no longer exists. Pilots without an Instrument Rating or, in the United Kingdom, an IMC Rating must not allow themselves to be vectored into IMC.

Pilots without Instrument Rating or, in the United Kingdom, an IMC Rating, must not allow themselves to be vectored into Instrument Meteorological Conditions (IMC).

   G-JM, Unknown traffic, 3 o'clock, 3 miles, Closing, Fast moving.

   Negative contact, Request vectors, G-JM.

G-JM, Turn right onto 360°.

Right, 360°, G-JM.

G-JM, Clear of traffic.

If there is an imminent risk of collision between an aircraft receiving a radar service and a second contact aircraft, the radar controller will instruct the pilot to take avoiding action. *(See Figures 7.4 and 7.5.)*

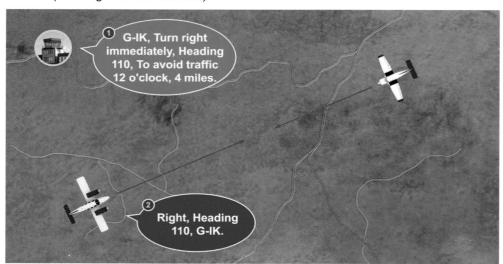

Figure 7.4.

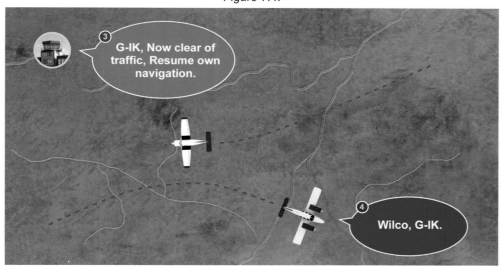

Figure 7.5.

SECONDARY SURVEILLANCE RADAR (SSR).

Secondary Surveillance Radar (SSR) is a means by which a radar controller can track the progress of an individually identified aircraft on his radar screen. The technical aspects and principle of operation of SSR are dealt with in Volume 3 of this series of books: 'Navigation'. SSR requires that an aircraft be fitted with a transmitter/receiver called a transponder on which the pilot sets a four-figure code allocated to him by ATC. When switched to 'ON', the equipment enables the aircraft's position to be identified on the ATC radar screen. The aircraft can then be individually identified and a radar service may be offered to the pilot.

With ALT selected, the aircraft's altitude is transmitted to the receiving radar unit. This flight level is based on 1013.2 hectopascals from an encoded altimeter fitted to the aircraft

When ALT is selected, the transponder is said to be operating in Mode Charlie.

When ON is selected, no altitude information is given on the controller's radar screen, and the transponder is said to be operating in Mode Alpha.

When a pilot has his transponder switched on, Mode Charlie (ALT) should always be selected, unless the radar controller instructs otherwise.

Mode Charlie (ALT) should always be selected on your transponder, unless a radar controller instructs otherwise.

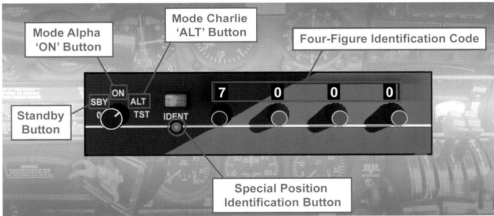

Figure 7.6 A Transponder.

The Conspicuity Code.

As we have mentioned, when instructed to do so by a radar controller, the pilot selects a 4-figure code on his transponder, allocated by the radar controller.

If a pilot is not communicating with an Air Traffic Control Unit (ATCU), or if the ATCU does not wish to allocate a discrete transponder code, national civil aviation authorities may publish a standard conspicuity code. The pilot may select this on his transponder so that an enhanced radar return from the aircraft is visible on the controller's screen, with Alpha or Charlie (altitude) information, even though no discrete code has been allocated to the aircraft

Different countries have different rules about conspicuity codes.

In the United Kingdom, the conspicuity code is 7000, unless in the vicinity of a busy aerodrome when 7010 may need to be selected.

In the United Kingdom, the conspicuity code is 7000, although in the vicinity of busy aerodromes, pilots may be requested to select 7010 by an ATSU.

THE BASIC LIGHT AIRCRAFT TRANSPONDER

The current types of basic transponder, carried by general aviation aircraft, mostly operates in two modes:

- Mode A. Mode Alpha is the name given to the basic transponder functionality which puts an identification code against the trace of an aircraft on the radar screen. The air traffic controller assigns the four-digit identification code (called a "squawk") to a pilot, over the radio, and the pilot selects the code on his transponder.

- Mode C. Transponders with a Mode Charlie functionality also transmit altitude information, based on the standard pressure setting of 1013.2 millibars (hectopascals) of an encoding altimeter, fitted to the aircraft.

  (A requirement for aircraft to carry transponders with a Mode S capability is being introduced in Europe. Mode S transponders will emit a signal which is unique to a particular aircraft and which stays with that aircraft throughout its operational life. Mode S is covered in more detail later in this chapter.)

On the standard light-aircraft transponder of the type depicted in *Figure 7.7*, selecting ON activates Mode A. Selecting ALT activates Mode C, alongside Mode A. If the aircraft is not fitted with an encoding altimeter, the transponder will function in Mode A only, even though there is an ALT position on the transponder. *Figure 7.7* depicts the transponder selected to ALT; with the selector in this position, the transponder is operating in both Mode C and Mode A.

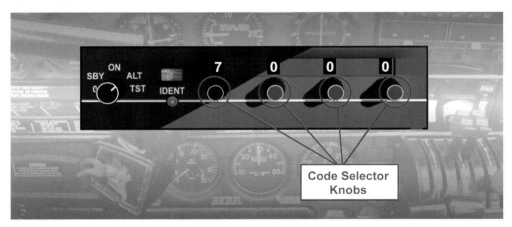

Figure 7.7 A transponder with Mode Charlie selected and squawking 4213.

If SBY, signifying STANDBY, is selected on the transponder, the instrument is switched on and is "warm", but the transponder functionality, itself, is not activated. In the SBY mode, the transponder functionality will, however, be instantly available as soon as the pilot moves the selector to the ON or ALT positions.

With the selector moved to the TEST position, the pilot can check whether the transponder is operating correctly. If the transponder is serviceable and functioning as it should, the transponder generates a self-interrogating signal and the REPLY-IDENT light illuminates.

The IDENT button activates the special position identification functionality of the transponder. The IDENT button is pressed by the pilot only on the request of the radar controller. When the pilot presses the IDENT button, a pulse is generated by the transponder which causes a particular display to appear, for several seconds, next to the aircraft's trace on the controller's radar screen, so that the controller can easily pick out the trace from other traces on his screen. When a controller wishes a pilot to activate the IDENT functionality, he will instruct the pilot to "Squawk Ident". The pilot complies by pressing briefly on the IDENT button, once only.

The transponder code or SQUAWK that a controller wishes a pilot to select on his transponder is a four-digit code passed to the pilot using words along the lines of "Squawk 4570". The pilot then uses each of the four code-selector knobs on the transponder set to select the required code. Because there are several special codes which signify emergency or equipment failure, when selecting a code the pilot must first switch the transponder to SBY, make his code selection, and then reselect ON or ALT, as appropriate.

SPECIAL TRANSPONDER CODES.

By international agreement some transponder codes are reserved for special purposes.

In an emergency, select 7700 on your transponder.

- **7700** indicates an **emergency condition**. This code should be selected by the pilot as soon as is practicable when declaring an **emergency**. However, if the aircraft is already transmitting an **assigned code**, and also receiving an air traffic service, the original code may be retained at the discretion of either the pilot or controller.

- **7600** indicates **radio failure**.

If you experience radio failure, select 7600 on your transponder.

- **7500** indicates that **unlawful interference** has occurred with the planned operation of the flight.

- **In the United Kingdom, 7000** is known as the **conspicuity code**. This code is squawked by an aircraft whose pilot has received no instructions from an ATC Unit to squawk an assigned code.

- In the United Kingdom, at aerodromes with a high concentration of visual circuit traffic, a specific VFR Aerodrome Traffic Pattern Conspicuity Code of 7010 may be requested by the ATSU. This is to facilitate greater exploitation of the collision avoidance "safety net" provided by Airborne Collision Avoidance Systems (ACAS), which are increasingly available to light aircraft. ACAS systems respond to SSR transmissions.

- On entering United Kingdom Airspace from an adjacent Flight Information Region (FIR) where a pilot has not been required to squawk a transponder code, the pilot should squawk the code 2000.

Squawk 2000, if you are entering United Kingdom Airspace from an adjacent FIR where you have not been required to squawk a transponder code.

MODE C should be operated with all of the above codes.

RADAR DISPLAYS OF TRANSPONDER RETURNS.

Figure 7.8 shows a radar display of aircraft movements in the London Terminal Control Area, where most of the traces are enhanced by SSR radar returns. The enlarged return shows a transponder - enhanced trace with the SSR information alongside it.

In *Figure 7.8* the aircraft's pilot-selected transponder code of 4570 is shown at the top of the information block. The radar controller will have instructed the pilot to select this four-digit code on the transponder. The digits 08 indicate that the aircraft is at Flight Level 80 (8000 feet above the pressure datum of 1013.2 millibars), and the digits S067 show that the aircraft has a groundspeed of 67 knots.

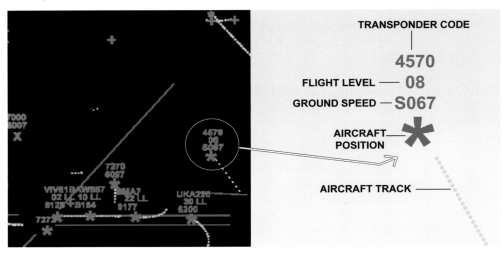

Figure 7.8 A typical ATC Radar display, with SSR enhanced traces.

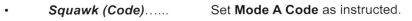

The following phrases may be used by a radar controller when transmitting instructions to a pilot concerning transponder settings.

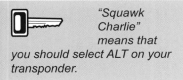
"Squawk Charlie" means that you should select ALT on your transponder.

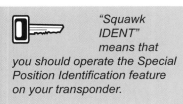
"Squawk IDENT" means that you should operate the Special Position Identification feature on your transponder.

- ***Squawk (Code)***…... Set **Mode A Code** as instructed.

- ***Confirm Squawk***… Confirm Mode and Code set on the transponder.

- ***Reset***…………..... Reselect the assigned Code.

- ***Squawk Ident***…..... Operate the **Special Position Identification (SPI)** functionality by pressing the **Ident button**.

- ***Squawk Mayday***…. Select Emergency (**Mode C, 7700**).

- ***Squawk Standby***… Select the **Standby (SBY)** position on your transponder.

- ***Squawk Charlie***….. Select **ALT** on your transponder.

- ***Check Altimeter and confirm level***. Check Pressure Setting & Report your level.

- ***Stop Squawk Charlie, wrong indication***. Deselect **ALT**, transmission faulty. Switch transponder to **ON**.

MODE S.

Although Secondary Surveillance Radar (SSR) gives air traffic controllers greater capability to ensure safe and effective surveillance of air traffic than Primary Surveillance Radar (PSR), alone, existing Mode A and Mode C SSRs do have some deficiencies. For instance, current SSR suffers from interference in the returns from aircraft which are on, or almost on, the same bearing from the ground station.

Figure 7.9 Mode S Transponder.

But, more importantly, when operating in Modes A or C, whether a transponder is selected to an assigned code or merely transmitting on the UK conspicuity code of 7000, all transponders in all aircraft within the coverage area of an SSR ground station are interrogated, on every sweep of the SSR radar head.

In order to overcome these and other deficiencies, Secondary Surveillance Radar, Mode S, a development and enhancement of classic SSR, is currently being introduced. Mode S radar surveillance will enable improved position determination of SSR targets while reducing the number of required replies by transponders, as well as improving other aspects of SSR functionality. A Mode S-equipped aircraft will have a unique identification code which will remain with the aircraft throughout its life. The selective nature of Mode S SSR means that air traffic control will be able to restrict interrogations to specified targets. Following initial acquisition and identification by a Mode S ground station, an aircraft will be subsequently interrogated in accordance with a specific "schedule" and not on every sweep of the SSR radar head. Furthermore, only the individually interrogated aircraft will respond.

Mode S, therefore, requires far fewer interrogations of aircraft than at present, in order to track an aircraft. This fact means that position reporting will be more accurate.

Additionally, Airborne Collision and Avoidance Systems (ACAS) work more efficiently in a wholly Mode S environment.

As mentioned above, the selective character of Mode S operations will also reduce problems associated with interference between transponder returns from aircraft on a similar bearing from the ground station, as well as interference caused by replies from one transponder responding to interrogations from another. This latter phenomenon is sometimes known as "Fruiting" (FRUIT = False Replies Unsynchronised In Time).

The United Kingdom Civil Aviation Authority is proposing that light aircraft operating in accordance with the Visual Flight Rules should be fitted with the elementary level of Mode S transponder when flying in uncontrolled airspace, and some classes of controlled airspace, by 31 March 2012. This is also a requirement within Europe.

The following examples of radio exchanges between a radar controller and a pilot will give you an idea of the type of RT transmissions you are likely to be involved in, regarding the operation of transponders. The reply by the pilot to the following instructions from the controller is usually either an acknowledgement or a readback.

G-CD, Advise capability of transponder.

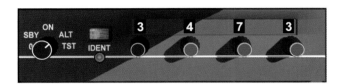

Transponder Charlie, G-CD.

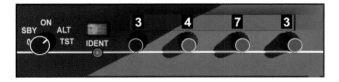

G-IK, Squawk 6411.

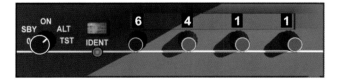

6411, G-IK.

The controller is instructing the pilot to set the SSR code 6411 on his transponder. Before setting the code, it would be sensible for the pilot to switch the transponder to STANDBY (SBY). Once 6411 has been set, the pilot switches the transponder back to ON or ALT. The ON position puts the transponder into Mode Alpha, the standard operating mode for aircraft identification. However, unless the controller has instructed the pilot not to squawk Mode Charlie (which provides altitude information alongside the SSR trace on the controller's radar screen), the pilot should select the ALT position with the selector knob.

G-JM, Confirm Squawk.

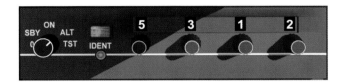

Squawking 5312, Mode Charlie, G-JM.

In response to the instruction CONFIRM SQUAWK, the pilot confirms the SSR code and operating mode (Alpha or Charlie) of his transponder.

G-JM, Reset 4213.

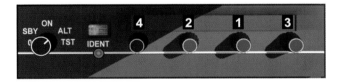

Resetting 4213, G-JM.

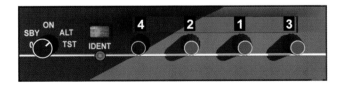

The instruction RESET is given by the radar controller when the correct SQUAWK does not appear on his radar screen, and the pilot is required to re-cycle the codes so that the same SQUAWK, in this case 4213, is reset on the transponder.

G-JM, Squawk Ident.

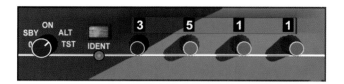

Squawk Ident, G-JM.

When instructed by air traffic control to SQUAWK IDENT, the pilot must press the IDENT button <u>once</u>, briefly, and release it. There is no need to keep the button pressed. Pressing the IDENT button causes a pulse, called a special position identification pulse, to be transmitted. This pulse transmits automatically for about 20 seconds, producing a distinct display on the controller's radar screen, enabling the controller to easily pick out the aircraft squawking IDENT from among other traces on his radar screen.

G-JM, Squawk Standby.

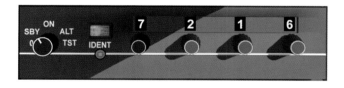

Squawk Standby, G-JM.

You may be instructed to SQUAWK STANDBY when the controller no longer wishes to see your squawk on his radar screen. In this case, the pilot moves the transponder's selector knob to the position marked by the letters SBY, signifying standby.

CHAPTER 8
COMMUNICATION FAILURE

INITIAL CHECKS IF RADIO FAILURE IS SUSPECTED.

On rare occasions, communications between aircraft and ground stations can break down. Communications failure can be caused by complete or partial failure of the radio equipment, but a common cause also is human error. For instance, the receiver volume may be turned down too low, or the wrong frequency selected.

Consequently, in the event of communications problems, you should first check your radio equipment to ensure that you are using it correctly. The following checks are good initial checks if you suspect that you have communications problems.

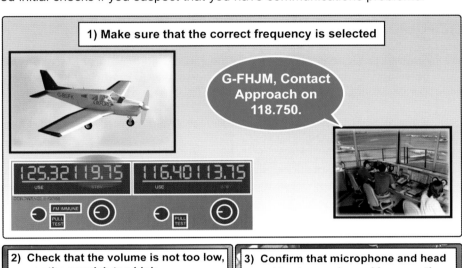

If you suspect that you have communications failure, check initially that:

- *the correct frequency is selected.*

- *the volume is turned up.*

- *the microphone and headset are plugged in correctly.*

- *the radio station is open.*

- *you are within range.*

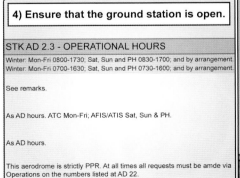

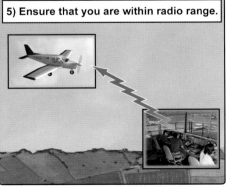

Figure 8.1.

If the above checks all appear satisfactory and you are still experiencing problems establishing two way communications with a ground station, the most likely cause is equipment failure, either in the aircraft or the ground station.

If you are operating in accordance with the Visual Flight Rules (VFR), the loss of communications will only become a significant problem if you are already receiving an air traffic service, or if you require a service such as joining an air traffic pattern.

If you do find that you are unable to establish communications with a ground station, you should adopt the following general procedure.

COMMUNICATIONS FAILURE PROCEDURE.

1) Attempt to establish contact with the ground station on another frequency published for that station. There may be several frequencies on which an Air Traffic Control Unit may be contacted: Tower, Approach, Radio, Ground.

2) If this attempt fails, attempt to establish communications with another station along the route being flown.

3) If that attempt is not successful, try to establish contact with other aircraft on frequencies appropriate to the route.

4) If no communication can be established, transmit your message twice on the original designated frequency, preceded by the words **TRANSMITTING BLIND**. This action is taken in case your transmitter is still operating and only the receiver has failed. Include the designator of the station addressed in your "blind" message.

When transmitting a message preceded by the words TRANSMITTING BLIND DUE TO RECEIVER FAILURE, the pilot should transmit each message twice, and advise the time of his next intended transmission.

5) If you know that it is your receiver which has failed, transmit reports or positions, at the scheduled times, on the frequency in use, preceded by the words **TRANSMITTING BLIND DUE TO RECEIVER FAILURE**. The content of your report should be pertinent to the safe continuation of your flight, and you should advise the time of your next intended transmission.

6) If you have a transponder, you should squawk 7600.

If you experience radio failure, select the code 7600 on your transponder.

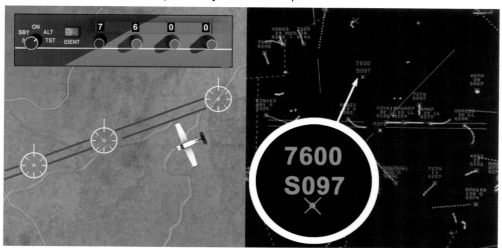

Figure 8.2 If you experience communications failure, and your aircraft is equipped with a transponder, squawk 7600.

7)   If it is only your transmitter which has failed, continue to listen out on the designated frequency. You may be able to answer questions from Air Traffic Control by using the radio's carrier wave, activated by the microphone. For instance, ATC may ask you to reply in the affirmative by pressing once, briefly, on your microphone button, or in the negative by pressing twice, briefly, on the microphone button.

A speechless code has been established within the United Kingdom, details of which are published in CAP 413.

RULES OF THE AIR CONCERNING COMMUNICATIONS FAILURE.

The Rules of the Air, as specified in Annex 2 to the ICAO Convention, stipulate that, when flying in accordance with the Visual Flight Rules, a pilot whose aircraft has suffered communications failure shall:

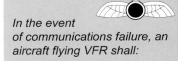

In the event of communications failure, an aircraft flying VFR shall:

- *continue to fly in VMC.*

- *squawk 7600, Mode C.*

- *land at the nearest suitable aerodrome.*

- *report arrival to ATC.*

    a.   Continue to fly in VMC.

    b.   If equipped with a transponder, squawk 7600, Mode Charlie.

    c.   Land at the nearest suitable aerodrome.

    d.   Report his arrival by the most expeditious means to the appropriate Air Traffic Services Unit.

A light aircraft pilot who had obtained prior permission to land at an aerodrome outside controlled airspace (that is, <u>not</u> a Control Zone), may, therefore, in the event of communications failure, possibly elect to continue to his destination, taking care to avoid controlled airspace and remaining in VMC.

When arriving at the destination airfield, with communications failure, the pilot must join the aerodrome circuit in the safest manner possible, given the conditions and air traffic situation at the destination aerodrome.

In the following example we will assume that the pilot has elected to make an overhead join. If airfield conditions allow an overhead join, this is often the safest join to make, because, when overhead the airfield, well above circuit height (see overleaf), the pilot has the best view of circuit traffic and of other indications of circuit direction, such as windsock and/or signal square.

Be aware though that many aerodromes do not permit an overhead join because of the mode of operation of the traffic using the aerodrome.

THE STANDARD OVERHEAD JOIN.

An aircraft, making a standard overhead join, should, initially:

- Overfly the aerodrome at 1 000 feet above published circuit height.

- Descend on the dead side to circuit height.

- Join the circuit by crossing the upwind end of the runway at circuit height.

- Position itself downwind.

The standard overhead join procedure is depicted in *Figure 8.3*.

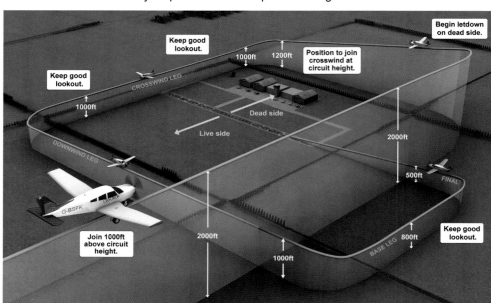

Figure 8.3 The Standard Overhead Join.

Position Reports.

If you have experienced radio failure, position reports should be made as depicted in *Figure 8.4*, but, in addition, each report should be made twice and be preceded by the words, **TRANSMITTING BLIND DUE TO RECEIVER FAILURE**.

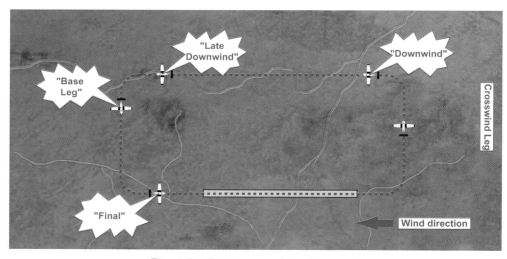

Figure 8.4 Position reports in the circuit.

If the airfield at which you were landing had full air traffic control, you would expect to obtain a clearance to land by light or flare (steady green light, or green flare). Of course, you must be prepared to receive a steady red light telling you that you must give way to other aircraft, in which case you would overshoot and rejoin the circuit.

Radio Failure Scenario.

We will assume that having suffered radio failure, you join Netherford, an airfield with an Air-Ground Communications Service, having already obtained prior permission to land there. You approach the airfield at approximately the time you had indicated when obtaining permission to fly to Netherford.

Netherford Radio, G-FHJM, Transmitting blind due to receiver failure, 10 miles East at 2 000ft, Joining for landing, Next transmission 45.

Netherford Radio, G-FHJM, Transmitting blind due to receiver failure, 10 miles East at 2 000ft, Joining for landing, Next transmission 45.

You would not know the QFE at Netherford, but if you were operating on a suitable QNH (Regional Pressure Setting in the United Kingdom) and knew the elevation of Netherford aerodrome, you would be able to deduce the circuit height from your airfield plate for Netherford. You would not, of course, know which runway was in use. Therefore, you would carry out an overhead join, if the Netherford airfield information does not prohibit it, and observe the windsock or signal square in order to determine which was the most likely active runway.

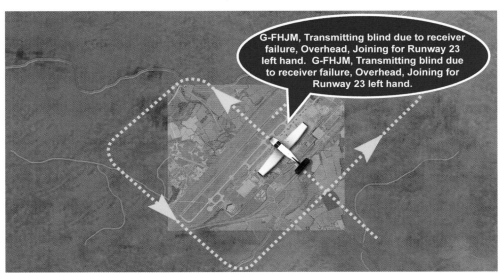

Figure 8.5 Communications failure - Overhead join transmission.

In the absence of any indications that there is a right hand circuit in force, the pilot should then carry out a visual, left-hand circuit, making his calls in the normal places. It is most likely that the aircraft would be observed by the ground station operator or controller as it manoeuvres in the circuit, and the operator would warn other aircraft that there is an aircraft in the circuit with apparent radio failure.

While in the circuit, the pilot should keep a close watch for instructions which may be issued by visual signals, such as lights or flares. A pilot can indicate to the ground that he has a problem by switching on and off his landing or navigation lights, in rapid succession.

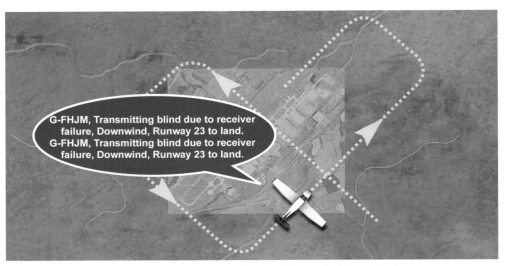

Figure 8.6 Communications failure - Downwind transmission.

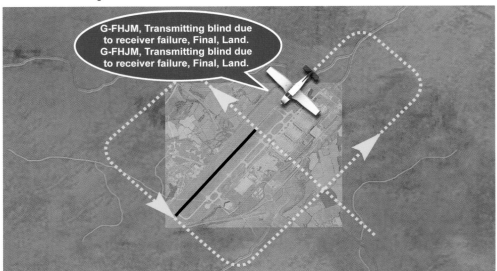

Figure 8.7 Communications failure - Final transmission.

After landing and shutdown, you should report to aerodrome control and give an account of the occurrence. By doing so you will have complied with the 2nd and 3rd rules of the ICAO Rules of the Air; that is, you will have landed at the nearest suitable aerodrome, and then reported your arrival by the most expeditious means to Air Traffic Control.

CHAPTER 9
DISTRESS AND
URGENCY

INTRODUCTION.

This chapter explains the RT phraseology procedures which a pilot should adopt when faced with an emergency situation, in the air.

Figure 9.1 An emergency situation in the air.

Although rare in modern aircraft, emergency situations in the air are mostly unexpected, and often frightening, and give little time for structured thought before action has to be taken by the pilot. Pilots must, therefore, become thoroughly familiar with the emergency procedures for any aircraft they fly.

You must be familiar with emergency procedures for any aircraft you fly.

Furthermore, pilots must be completely familiar with standard emergency RT procedures and phraseology. RT is the only means a pilot has of summoning outside help in an emergency, so emergency transmissions must be made quickly and correctly. There will not be time for a protracted and considered RT transmission, during an actual emergency.

The two states of emergency are DISTRESS and URGENCY.

DISTRESS AND URGENCY.

In the context of aircraft operations, airborne emergencies are defined as states of **DISTRESS** or **URGENCY**. The definition of **DISTRESS** and **URGENCY** are as follows:

MAYDAY x 3 is the prefix for a distress call. PAN PAN x 3 is the prefix for an urgency call.

DISTRESS. A condition of being threatened by serious and/or imminent danger and of requiring immediate assistance. (MAYDAY, MAYDAY, MAYDAY.)

URGENCY. A condition concerning the safety of an aircraft or other vehicle, or of some person on board or within sight, but which does not require immediate assistance. (PAN PAN, PAN PAN, PAN PAN.)

Figure 9.2 Definitions of distress and urgency situations.

- If your aircraft is in **Distress**, your RT message must be prefixed by the phrase **MAYDAY MAYDAY MAYDAY.**

- If the situation is one of Urgency, your RT message should be prefixed by the phrase PAN PAN, PAN PAN, PAN PAN.

Factors to Bear in Mind When Making an Emergency Transmission.

There are a number of factors which you must bear in mind when making an **emergency call**. These are intended to ensure that your message is heard and understood clearly and unambiguously, so that effective assistance may be promptly rendered.

- **Distress messages have priority over all other transmissions**.

- Urgency **messages have priority over all transmissions except** distress **messages**.

- When making **distress** or urgency calls, you should speak slowly and clearly, and avoid any unnecessary repetition.

- You should adapt the **emergency phraseology** detailed on the next page to your specific needs, and to the time available.

- Always seek assistance immediately there is serious doubt about the safety of the flight. By reacting promptly and appropriately, the risk of a more serious situation developing may be avoided.

- If you have time, select the **emergency code** of **7700** on your transponder, before you make your emergency transmission.

- Make your **distress** or urgency call on the frequency in use at the time and continue to use that frequency unless more effective assistance can be obtained on another frequency.

- **121.5 MHz** is the international aeronautical emergency frequency. This frequency should be used if no effective assistance is offered by the controller on the frequency you are in contact with, at the time the emergency occurs.

SQUAWK 7700 if you are in a distress situation.

In the first instance, the pilot should make a distress or urgency call on the frequency in use at the time.

Pilots hearing transmissions pertaining to an emergency situation being made on the frequency they have been working should make no further transmissions on that frequency, unless directly involved in rendering assistance, or **until the emergency has ended**.

If a pilot intercepts a distress message which apparently receives no acknowledgement, he should acknowledge the message and then re-broadcast it to the ground station being addressed.

*The international aeronautical emergency frequency is **121.5 MHz**. Pilots experiencing an emergency should use this frequency, if they obtain no effective assistance on the frequency with which they are in contact when the emergency occurs.*

DISTRESS.

A distress message should contain as many as possible of the following elements.

a) Name of the station addressed (time and circumstances permitting).

b) Identification of the aircraft (call-sign and type).

c) Nature of the distress condition.

d) Intention of the person in command.

e) Present (or last known) position, level or altitude, and heading.

f) Pilot qualification*.

g) Any other useful information (number of persons on board, endurance, etc).

Figure 9.3.

In a distress call, immediately following the MAYDAY prefix, the pilot, if time and circumstances permit, should transmit the call-sign of the station addressed.

* You should note that pilot qualification is not a standard element of the ICAO pattern of distress message, but should be included in the United Kingdom. Information on pilot qualification may help a controller plan a course of action which fits the pilot's qualification.

When transmitting an emergency message, a pilot is required to give his aircraft's position as his present, or last known, position, together with his level or altitude, and heading.

MAYDAY MAYDAY MAYDAY, Steerton Tower, G-FHJM, PA28, Engine on fire, Making forced landing 10 miles South of Steerton, Passing 3000ft, heading 360, PPL, 2 POB.

G-FHJM, Steerton Tower, Roger MAYDAY, Surface wind at Steerton 230°, 10 knots, Steerton QNH 998.

MAYDAY MAYDAY MAYDAY, Steerton Tower, G-ABCD, Engine failed, Will attempt to land at your field, Present position 5 miles East of Steerton, 4000ft, heading 270, PPL, 2 POB.

G-ABCD, Steerton Tower, Roger MAYDAY, Cleared to land Runway 20, Wind 210 degrees 12 knots, QNH 1008, You are number one.

Imposition of Silence.

A station in control of an aircraft in distress, may impose silence, either on all aircraft on the frequency or on a particular aircraft which may be interfering with the distress situation. Aircraft on which silence is imposed should maintain radio silence until advised that the distress traffic has ended.

All stations, Steerton Tower, Stop transmitting, MAYDAY in progress.

Cancelling a Distress Message.

If a **distress** condition is resolved, the pilot should transmit a message cancelling the **distress** condition.

Steerton Tower, G-CD, Cancel distress, Engine re-started, Field in sight, Request landing.

G-CD, Runway 20, Wind 210 degrees, 10 knots, Cleared to land.

Runway 20, Cleared to land, G-CD.

Termination of Distress Traffic.

When a ground station which is controlling an aircraft in distress becomes aware that the aircraft is no longer in distress, the ground station will terminate the distress communication and silence condition.

All stations, Steerton Tower, Distress traffic ended.

URGENCY.

An urgency message should contain as many of the elements of the **distress message** as are required by the urgency situation. The urgency message should be transmitted **on the frequency being used** by the pilot at the time the emergency occurs. All other traffic should take care not to interfere with urgency transmissions.

PAN PAN, PAN PAN, PAN PAN, Steerton Tower, G-FHJM, Warrior, Above cloud and unsure of position, Request heading to Steerton, Altitude 2 000 feet, Heading 190, PPL, No Instrument Qualification, Endurance 2 hours.

G-FHJM, Steerton Tower, Steer heading 160.

Heading 160, G-FHJM.

PAN PAN, PAN PAN, PAN PAN, Steerton Tower, G-ABCD, Cessna 172, Passenger with suspected heart attack, Request priority landing, Present position 5 miles North of Steerton, 1 500 feet, QNH 1006, Heading 180, 3 POB.

G-CD, Walden Steerton, Runway 20, Wind 210 degrees, 12 knots, QNH 1008, Make straight in approach, Ambulance requested.

Relaying an Urgency Message.

The following is an example of an urgency message being relayed by another aircraft, because the emergency aircraft cannot hear the reply from the ground station.

PAN PAN, PAN PAN, PAN PAN, Steerton Tower, G-FHJM, Intercepted urgency call from G-ABCD, Passenger with suspected heart attack, Requesting priority landing at Steerton. His position is 5 miles North of Steerton at 1 500 feet.

G-JM, Steerton Tower, Roger.

Steerton Tower, having acknowledged receipt of the relayed message from G-FHJM, would then re-transmit their reply to G-ABCD in response to G-ABCD's urgency message. If G-ABCD still does not acknowledge receipt of Steerton Tower's message, Steerton Tower would ask G-FHJM to relay the message.

USE OF 121.5 MHZ IN THE UNITED KINGDOM.

In the United Kingdom, the international emergency frequency, 121.5 MHz, is manned by Royal Air Force personnel. An emergency service is available continuously on 121.5 MHz to pilots flying within United Kingdom airspace, who are in distress, in urgent need of assistance, are lost, or temporarily unsure of their position.

See Chapter 13 for further details of the position fixing service available on 121.5 MHz in the United Kingdom.

When using 121.5 MHz in the United Kingdom to transmit a distress or urgency message, pilots should address the emergency call to London Centre, when South of Latitude 55°N, and Scottish Centre, when North of Latitude 55°N.

Once two-way communication has been established, pilots should not leave 121.5 MHz, without telling the controller.

CHAPTER 10
VHF PROPAGATION

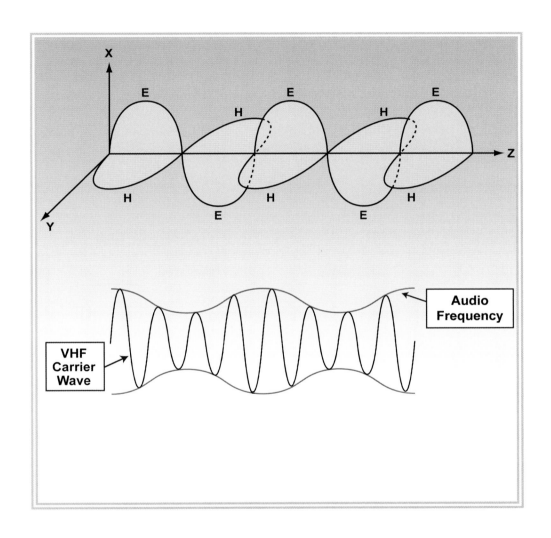

INTRODUCTION.

Radio propagation is a term used to explain how radio waves behave when they are broadcast from one point on the Earth to another.

Radio waves are electromagnetic waves on which audio frequencies are superimposed by a process known as modulation.

Electromagnetic Waves.

If an alternating current of a suitably high frequency is fed to a transmitting aerial, the energy of the current is not contained within the aerial but radiates out into space in the form of electromagnetic waves. This radiation of energy through space comprises alternating electrical and magnetic fields at right angles to each other. The amplitude of each field varies (oscillates) between zero and a maximum value, at the same frequency as the alternating current in the aerial.

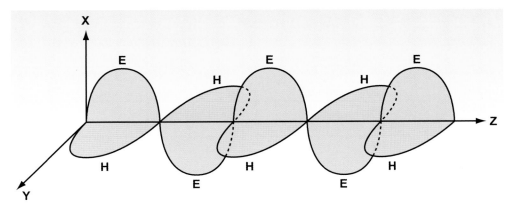

Figure 10.1 A representation of an electromagnetic wave showing the alternating electrical and magnetic fields at right angles to each other.

Electromagnetic radiation of this kind is classified into types according to the frequency (cycles per second) of the wave. In order of increasing frequency, electromagnetic waves are classified as:

*   radio waves.
*   microwaves.
*   terahertz radiation.
*   infrared radiation.
*   visible light.
*   ultra violet radiation.
*   x-rays.
*   gamma rays.

The Propagation of Electromagnetic Waves.

Electromagnetic radiation is a form of energy. Electromagnetic waves travel in straight lines, but their propagation is modified by interaction with the Earth's surface and by reflection, refraction and diffraction within the atmosphere, especially by reflection within the ionosphere.

Frequency Units.

The frequencies of all electromagnetic waves are expressed in Hertz (Hz). One Hertz equals one cycle per second. Radio frequencies are high and so their frequencies are measured in thousands or millions of cycles per second.

1 Kilo-Hertz (kHz)	= 1,000 Hz	= 10^3 Hz
1 Mega-Hertz (MHz)	= 1,000,000 Hz	= 10^6 Hz
1 Giga-Hertz (GHz)	= 10^9 Hz	
1 Tera-Hertz (THz)	= 10^{12} Hz	

Radio Frequency Bands.

The following table shows the division of radio frequencies into the various bands. The bands used for radio voice communications are the Very High Frequency (VHF) and the High Frequency (HF) bands.

Frequencies	Band	Wavelength	Uses
3-30 kHz	VLF (Very Low Frequency)	100 - 10 km	Very long range navigation
30 - 300 kHz	LF (Low Frequency)	10 - 1 km	NDB, Decca, Loran-C
300 - 3000 kHz	MF (Medium Frequency)	1 km - 100 m	NDB
3 - 30 MHz	HF (High Frequency)	100 - 10 m	HF RT
30 - 300 MHz	VHF (Very High Frequency)	10 - 1 m	VHF RT, VDF, VOR, ILS, marker beacons
300 - 3000 MHz	UHF (Ultra High Frequency)	1m - 10 cm	ILS Glidepath, DME, some surveillance radars
3 - 30 GHz	SHF (Super High Frequency)	10 - 1 cm	PAR, some surveillance radar, radio altimeter
30 - 300 GHz	EHF (Extremely High Frequency)	1 cm - 1 mm	Airfield Surface Movement Radar

The following table shows the **frequencies** in the **VHF** band which are of concern to the general aviation pilot.

Frequencies	Use
88 - 107.95 MHz	Broadcasting (AM & FM)
108 - 117.975 MHz	Radio Navigation (ILS & VOR)
118 - 136.975 MHz	Radio Communication (This is the band that is used for VHF voice communications)

Unlike lower frequency waves, Very High Frequency (VHF) radio waves are not reflected by the ionosphere. Radio frequencies above 30 MHz can penetrate the ionosphere making them unsuitable for long distance propagation.

Consequently VHF waves with frequencies from 30 to 300 MHz are mainly used for line-of-sight communication. VHF is also less affected by atmospheric noise and interference from electrical equipment than lower frequencies.

VHF radio frequencies are used for line-of-sight communication.

VHF Radio Transmission.

Within the VHF aviation voice communication wave band, the basic VHF radio wave, called a carrier wave, is modified through a process known as amplitude modulation in order to "superimpose" the voice information on the carrier wave generated by the aircraft or ground station radio "transceiver" (transmitter/receiver.)

When the pilot speaks into the microphone of his aircraft's radio, and presses on the radio's press-to-talk button, the output frequency wave which has been dialled up on the radio (say, 136.975, as depicted in *Figure 10.5*) is modulated by the audio frequencies from the microphone.

Amplitude Modulation (AM) of the carrier wave takes up less bandwidth than Frequency Modulation (FM), and so AM channel spacing in the aviation voice communication band can be narrow. The bandwidth allocated to VHF frequencies (i.e. the spacing between one selectable frequency and another) is, at present, for the most part, 25kHz (0.025MHz). However, as mentioned in Chapter 1, this is being reduced to 8.33kHz (one third of 25kHz) for aircraft operating above Flight Level 195, over Europe.

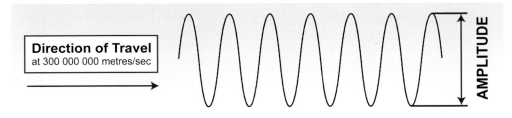

Figure 10.2. A VHF Carrier Wave.

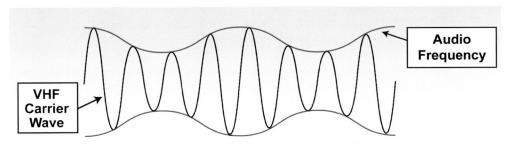

Figure 10.3. The VHF carrier wave modulated in amplitude by audio frequencies from the radio microphone.

VHF Radio Reception.

An aircraft antenna (*see Figure 10.4*) will continuously pick up the VHF radio frequency waves of the bandwidth for which the antenna is designed.

Figure 10.4. VHF 1 and VHF 2 Aerials.

The radio's receiver filters out all the frequencies except the frequency which the pilot has selected on his radio, (such as 136.975, as depicted in *Figure 10.5*.) The selected frequency is then "demodulated" by the receiver in order to isolate the voice information from the carrier wave. The demodulated frequency, now an audio frequency, is amplified and passed to the earphones of the pilot's headset which convert the audio frequency to sound waves audible to the pilot.

Figure 10.5.

Speed of Propagation.

All electromagnetic waves are propagated at the speed of light: 300 000 000 metres per second, or 162 000 nautical miles per second.

VHF PROPAGATION CHARACTERISTICS

As we have mentioned, propagation of radio waves in the VHF band (30 MHz to 300 MHz) is, principally, straight line propagation. VHF radio transmissions are also relatively <u>unaffected</u> by reflection, refraction and diffraction within the atmosphere. VHF transmissions are, however, heavily attenuated by the Earth's surface, and are blocked, diffracted or reflected by terrain.

VHF signal strength is inversely proportional to the distance from the transmitting station.

Attenuation.

The term attenuation means loss in strength of a radio signal as range from the transmitter increases. The signal strength received is inversely proportional to the distance from the transmitter. A wave becomes attenuated as range increases because:

- The radio energy available is spread over a greater area.

- Radio energy is lost to the Earth, the atmosphere, and sometimes to the ionised layers above the Earth.

The energy of the transmitted radio wave must be high enough to prevent attenuation over the line-of-sight range of the wave. Consequently the operational range of a VHF radio emission also depends on the power of the transmitter. Range is proportional to the square of the transmitter power. For example, if the range is to be doubled, the transmitter power must be quadrupled.

Line of Sight Range.

As VHF radio waves are subjected to the line-of-sight principle, the curvature of the Earth will limit the range of VHF radio. The aircraft below the horizon in *Figure 10.6* will not pick up the transmission from the aerial depicted.

Horizon Ray

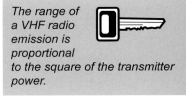

The range of a VHF radio emission is proportional to the square of the transmitter power.

Figure 10.6. VHF Line-of-sight ray.

The lowest wave able to be received by the aircraft is just tangential to the Earth's surface and is known as the horizon ray. Communication with the aircraft depicted could be achieved by either increasing the height of the transmission aerial or by the aircraft gaining altitude.

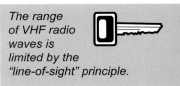

The range of VHF radio waves is limited by the "line-of-sight" principle.

For good reception of a VHF transmission there must be a direct line-of-sight path between the transmitter antenna and the receiver antenna.

The range of VHF transmissions can be estimated by using the following formula:

Signal Range = 1.25 ($\sqrt{h_1}$ + $\sqrt{h_2}$) nautical miles.

where

h_1 = receiver altitude **in feet,** and h_2 = transmitter elevation **in feet**

So, in air-to-air communications, the line-of-sight range of a VHF transmission from a ground station, whose elevation we will take to be negligible (i.e. approximating to 0 feet) and an aircraft at 5000 feet will be given by the equation:

Signal Range = 1.25 × $\sqrt{5000}$ = 1.25 × 71 = approximately 89 nautical miles.

Be aware that the line-of-sight range is the theoretical maximum range for direct path VHF transmission/reception. The actual range will probably be lower, being also dependent on factors such as the characteristics of the transmitter system, the type, position and orientation of the antenna, the quality of the receiver/headset, and so on.

Wave Propagation Paths.

The path of VHF radio waves travelling from a transmitter to a receiver, many miles away, is not always a direct path only. Often, the signal may be reaching the receiver by more than one path at the same time, and because of the different path lengths there will be phase differences between the signals. Such phase differences affect the received signal strength. For instance, if two waves from the same transmitter travel by different paths and arrive 180° out of phase, they will cancel each other out, if they are of equal amplitude. The resultant signal strength will be zero, so no signal will be received. Changes in phase difference of this kind will cause changes in signal strength, producing an effect known as fading.

A signal which travels in a straight line between transmitter and receiver is called the direct wave. In addition to this, there is normally a signal arriving at the receiver after reflection at the Earth's surface. This is the ground-reflected wave. These two waves are jointly known as the space wave. *(See Figure 10.7.)*

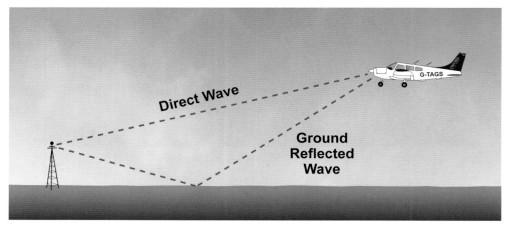

Figure 10.7 The direct and ground reflected-wave forming the space wave.

CHAPTER 11
WEATHER INFORMATION

WEATHER INFORMATION.

As well as meteorological reports and forecasts being available to the pilot for flight planning purposes prior to getting airborne, weather information can also be obtained in flight, over the radio. Information on how the weather situation is developing, in the form of reports, forecasts, or warnings, is made available to pilots using the aeronautical mobile service, either by broadcasts on specific frequencies, such as VOLMET, or from ground stations which offer a Flight Information Service to pilots.

Weather information can be obtained by pilots, when airborne, in several ways, including using VOLMET, or through a Flight Information Service.

Figure 11.1 Information on the developing weather situation is available in flight, over the radio.

These weather broadcasts enable a pilot to update his plans and intentions for the continuation of his flight, should the need arise.

SOURCES OF WEATHER INFORMATION.

A pilot in flight can obtain weather information from several sources. The main sources are listed below:

An Automatic Terminal Information Service (ATIS) is available at most large aerodromes.

From Air Traffic Service Units.
The weather conditions at a particular aerodrome may be obtained by a pilot, when airborne, from the aerodrome's Air Traffic Service Unit, on request, usually on the airfield approach frequency.

 Walden Approach, G-EGIK, Request your weather.

G-IK Walden Approach, Present weather, Wind 360 degrees 5 knots, Visibility 20 kms, Cloud 2 oktas 2500 feet, QNH 1008.

QNH 1008, G-IK.

Notice that the pilot must repeat only the QNH. The active runway will be included in the broadcast if the pilot is intending to join the circuit. If the runway-in-use is included, then its designation should also be read back by the pilot.

Automatic Terminal Information Service (ATIS).

When an aerodrome has a frequency devoted to an Automatic Terminal Information Service (ATIS), a pilot may obtain weather information for that aerodrome on the ATIS frequency. ATIS is a transmission of current aerodrome information, broadcast continuously during the aerodrome's operating hours. ATIS is usually available at large and intermediate size aerodromes. ATIS frequencies can be obtained from national Aeronautical Information Publications (Aerodrome Section), as well as from commercially produced flight guides.

The ATIS is usually transmitted on a discrete VHF frequency for each airport, although at some aerodromes there will be an ATIS for departure, and another for arrival. An example of the availability of ATIS at Manchester Airport is depicted in *Figure 11.2* which is an extract from the UK AIP (Aerodromes).

EGCC AD 2.18 - ATS COMMUNICATION FACILITIES					
Service Designation	Callsign	Frequency MHz	Hours of Operation Winter	Summer	Remarks
1	2	3	4		5
APP	Manchester Radar	119.525†	H24	H24	ATZ hours coincident with Approach hours.
	Manchester Radar	118.575	As directed by ATC	As directed by ATC	†Serves Manchester and Manchester
	Manchester Director	121.350			Woodford
TWR	Manchester Tower	118.625 121.500‡ 119.400	H24	H24	‡Emergency Ch O/R
	Manchester Ground	121.850 121.700§ 125.375	0630-2200 2200-0630 As directed by ATC	0530-2100 2100-0530 As directed by ATC	§Departing aircraft are to make initial call on 121.700 MHz to 'Manchester Delivery' or Manchester 'ground' as appropriate.
	Manchester Delivery	121.700§	0630-2200	0530-2100	
Arrival ATIS^Ø	Manchester Information	128.175	H24	H24	^ØAlso available by telephone 0161-499 2324
Departure ATIS^Ø	Manchester Departure Information	121.975	0520-2220	0420-2120	Non-ATS frequency.
FIRE	Manchester Fire	121.600	Available when Fire vehicle attending aircraft on the ground in an emergency		

Figure 11.2 Manchester Airport is one of a few airports that have separate frequencies for arrival and departure ATIS.

Sometimes, in order to free up air traffic VHF communication frequencies, some aerodromes transmit ATIS information on the voice channel of a VOR beacon at the aerodrome. *Figure 11.3*, extracted from the UK AIP, shows that, at Southampton Airport, ATIS is broadcast on the Southampton VOR frequency.

EGHI AD 2.18 - ATS COMMUNICATION FACILITIES					
Service Designation	Callsign	Frequency MHz	Hours of Operation		Remarks
			Winter	Summer	
1	2	3	4		5
APP	Southampton Approach	128.850	As directed by ATC	As directed by ATC	ATZ hours coincident with Tower hours (but not by arrangement).
TWR	Southampton Tower	118.200	†Mon - Fri 0525-2100 Sat 0625-2000 Sun 0735-2100 and by arrangement	†Mon - Thu 0545-2030 Fri 0545-2115 Sat 0630-1915 Sun 0800-2000 and by arrangement	†Hours subject to change, consult latest NOTAM.
RAD	Southampton Ground	121.775	As directed by ATC		
	Southampton Radar	128.550	As directed by ATC		
ATIS	Southampton Information	113.350	HO	HO	Broadcast on Southampton VOR
FIRE	Southampton Fire	121.600	Available when Fire vehicle attending aircraft on the ground in an emergency		Non-ATS frequency

Figure 11.3 Southampton Airport is an example of an airfield at which the ATIS is broadcast on the VOR frequency.

As weather conditions change, the ATIS is immediately updated and re-recorded to reflect the changes. Each new, updated ATIS broadcast is given a sequential alphabetical code, which supersedes the previous recording. For example, ATIS broadcast BRAVO will have replaced the previous ATIS broadcast ALPHA. When first contacting to Air Traffic Control (ATC) on arrival at, or departure from, an aerodrome, the pilot is required to state the letter code of the ATIS information last received, in order that ATC may verify that the pilot has the most recent ATIS information.

ATIS is broadcast in plain language and contains some, or all of the following information.

- Aerodrome name.

- ATIS sequence designator or information code.

- Time of observation.

- Runway in use and status.

- Surface wind in knots.

- Visibility and Runway Visual Range.

- Present weather.

- Significant cloud.

- Temperature and dew point.

•   Altimeter setting.

•   Any warnings pertinent to flight operations.

The ATIS permits the pilot to plan an efficient departure from, or arrival at, an aerodrome.

Obtaining the ATIS will also ensure that radio transmissions between Air Traffic Control and the pilot are kept to a minimum. This is especially important in busy air space where it is desirable that radio transmissions be kept short, to allow for effective communication between ATC and all the aircraft in the vicinity.

VOLMET.

VOLMET broadcasts are ground-to-air HF or VHF transmissions of meteorological reports and forecasts. VOLMET broadcasts follow a standard format, and contain weather information, in plain language, for a group of aerodromes, between published times. Information about VOLMET broadcasts and their frequencies can be found in national aeronautical information publications.

VOLMET transmissions give the latest weather reports, such as METARs. Recently, however, more information has been added to the VOLMET transmissions, which may now include SIGMETS and TAFS.

Using VOLMET can be time-consuming for the light aircraft pilot, because VOLMET broadcasts weather information for a number of different aerodromes sequentially. As a result, the pilot has to wait for the forecast for the aerodrome pertinent to his flight to come around. However, VOLMET remains an important source of aeronautical weather information for the general aviation pilot.

Figure 11.4, extracted from the UK AIP (GEN), shows the list of VHF VOLMET services for the United Kingdom and the near continent.

GEN 3.5.7 - VOLMET SERVICES						
Table 3.5.7.1 - Meteorological Radio Broadcasts (VOLMET)						
Call Sign/ID	EM	Frequency MHz	Operating Hours	Stations	Contents	Remarks
1	2	3	4	5	6	7
London Volmet (Main)	A3E	135.375	H24 continuous	Amsterdam Brussels Dublin Glasgow London Gatwick London Heathrow London Stansted Manchester Paris Charles de Gaulle	(1) Half hourly reports (METAR) (2) The elements of each report broadcast in the following order: (a) Surface wind (b) Visibility (or CAVOK) (c) RVR if applicable (d) Weather (e) Cloud (or CAVOK) (f) Temperature (g) Dewpoint (h) QNH (i) Recent Weather if applicable (j) Windshear if applicable (k) TREND if applicable (l) Runway Contamination Warning if applicable (3) Non-essential words such as 'surface wind', 'visibility' etc are not spoken. (4) Except for 'SNOCLO' (see Column 7), the Runway State Group is not broadcast. (5) All broadcasts are in English.	The spoken word 'SNOCLO' will be added to the end of the aerodrome report when that aerodrome is unusable for take-offs and landings due to heavy snow on runways, or runway snow clearance.
London Volmet (South)	A3E	128.600	H24 continuous	Birmingham Bournemouth Bristol Cardiff Jersey London Luton Norwich Southampton Southend		
London Volmet (North) (Note 1)	A3E	126.600	H24 continuous	Blackpool East Midlands Isle of Man Leeds Bradford Liverpool London Gatwick Manchester Newcastle Teesside		
Scottish Volmet	A3E	125.725	H24 continuous	Aberdeen/Dyce Belfast Aldegrove Edinburgh Glasgow Inverness London Heathrow Prestwick Stornoway		
Note 1: Broadcasting Range extended to cover Southeast England and English Channel						
Note 2: An HF VOLMET broadcast for North Atlantic flights (Shannon VOLMET) is operated by the Republic of Ireland						

Figure 11.4 VHF VOLMET Services in the United Kingdom.

You will notice that there are four UK VOLMET stations: LONDON VOLMET MAIN, LONDON VOLMET NORTH, LONDON VOLMET SOUTH and the SCOTTISH VOLMET. Next to each of these is the frequency on which the transmission may be found, the operating hours, and the aerodromes covered by the broadcast. The London VOLMET Main broadcast, for example, is broadcast on a VHF frequency of 135.375 MHz, continuously over a 24 hour period.

Figure 11.5 shows a partial text version of a London VOLMET Main broadcast. Six of the major aerodromes from the broadcast are listed, with their associated weather information.

THIS IS LONDON VOLMET MAIN **AMSTERDAM** AT 1125. WIND 160 DEGREES 16 KNOTS. VARIABLE BETWEEN 130 AND 190 DEGREES. VISIBILITY 7 KILOMETRES. LIGHT RAIN SHOWERS. CLOUD FEW 2 THOUSAND FEET. FEW CUMULONIMBUS 2 THOUSAND 5 HUNDRED FEET. BROKEN 4 THOUSAND FEET. TEMPERATURE 14. DEWPOINT 9 QNH 1004 BECOMING VISIBILITY 10 KILOMETRES OR MORE. NIL SIGNIFICANT WEATHER.	**BRUSSELS** AT 1120 WIND 190 DEGREES 14 KNOTS MAXIMUM 24 KNOTS. VISIBILITY 10 KILOMETRES OR MORE. LIGHT RAIN SHOWERS. CLOUD SCATTERED 2 THOUSAND 3 HUNDRED FEET. SCATTERED 5 THOUSAND FEET. BROKEN 10 THOUSAND FEET. TEMPERATURE 13. DEWPOINT 10. QNH 1006. NOSIG.
GLASGOW AT 1120. WIND 070 DEGREES 5 KNOTS. VARIABLE BETWEEN 030 AND 110 DEGREES. VISIBILITY 10 KILOMETRES OR MORE. CLOUD FEW 1 THOUSAND 8 HUNDRED FEET SCATTERED 4 THOUSAND 5 HUNDRED FEET. TEMPERATURE 14. DEWPOINT 8. QNH 997.	**DUBLIN** AT 1130. WIND 260 DEGREES 6 KNOTS. VARIABLE BETWEEN 240 AND 300 DEGREES. VISIBILITY 10 KILOMETRES OR MORE. CLOUD SCATTERED 2 THOUSAND 4 HUN-DRED FEET. TEMPERATURE 13. DEWPOINT 6. QNH 997. NOSIG.
LONDON/GATWICK AT 1120. WIND 190 DEGREES 10 KNOTS. VARIABLE BETWEEN 150 AND 220 DEGREES. VISIBILITY 10 KILOMETRES OR MORE. SHOWERS IN VICINITY. CLOUD FEW CUMULONIMBUS 2 THOUSAND 4 HUNDRED SCATTERED 4 THOUSAND FEET. TEMPERATURE 11. DEWPOINT 9. QNH 999.	**LONDON/HEATHROW** AT 1120. WIND 220 DEGREES 12 KNOTS. VARIABLE BETWEEN 190 AND 250 DEGREES. VISIBILITY 10 KILOMETRES OR MORE. LIGHT RAIN SHOWERS. CLOUD FEW 2 THOUSAND FEET. BROKEN 11 THOUSAND FEET. TEMPERATURE 11. DEWPOINT 8. QNH 997. TEMPO VISIBILITY 4 THOUSAND 5 HUNDRED METRES. RAIN SHOWERS.

Figure 11.5 Extract from a London VOLMET Main broadcast.

VOLMET transmissions are designed to be simple and easily understood, so that fast, efficient weather briefing can be obtained whilst in-flight. During pre-flight planning, pilots should note down the VOLMET frequencies for the areas in which they plan to fly so that, en-route, they can get hold of the latest weather information for airfields in the vicinity of destination and alternate airfields.

amazon.co.uk®

Thank you for shopping at Amazon.co.uk!

Invoice for
Your order of 5 November, 2011
Order ID 026-397497-619,564
Invoice number D5YKHwJN
Invoice date 5 No,ember, 2011

Billing Address
Dr. Orhan Ertug...
3 Watersi.de Close
Andover,shire, Gloucestershire GL54 4LG
United Kingdom

Shipping Address
Mrs S M Ertug,hn,l
o,. Leupold Road
East Finchley
London N2 8BG
United Kingdom

Qty.	Item	Our Price (excl VAT)	VAT Rate	Total Price
1	Radiotelephony for PPL and Beyond Radiotelephony v. 7: ICAO Procedures, £21.80 VFR RT Communications, Uk Procedures (Skills to... Paperback 0955517761 (** [*1-D28D315 *,*)		£21.80	

Shipping charges		£0.00	0%	£0.00
Subtotal (excl VAT)				£21.80
Total VAT				£0.00
Total				£21.80

Conversion rate - £1.00 . EUR 1.16

This shipment completes your order.

You can always check the status of your orders, or make changes to your account details from the 'Your Account' link at the top left of each page on our site.

Thinking of returning an item? PLEASE USE OUR ON-LINE RETURNS SUPPORT CENTRE.

Our Returns Support Centre (www.amazon.co.uk/returns-support) will guide you through our Returns Policy and provide you with a printable personalised return label. Please have your order number ready (you can find it next to your order summary above). Our Returns Policy does not affect your statutory rights.

Amazon EU S.à r.l, 5 Rue Plaetis, L-2338, Luxembourg
VAT number : 0972255921

Please note - this is not a returns address - for returns - please see above for details of our online returns centre

16/DrYrHwJN/-1 of 1 //1M/premium-uk/S4*/0243/1106-14.00/1106-12 16/yghebrey Pack Type : C4

CHAPTER 12
VFR FLIGHT SCENARIO

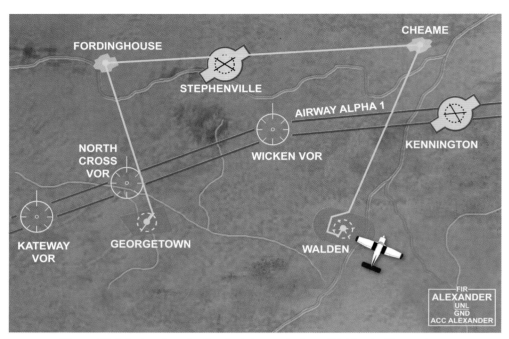

Figure 12.1 A visual navigation training route from Walden to Georgetown.

Station	Frequency
Walden ATIS	121.750
Walden Ground	121.950
Walden Tower	118.750
Walden Approach	125.325
Kennington Approach	128.950
Alexander Information	125.750
Stephenville Radar	128.150
Georgetown Approach	120.625
Georgetown Tower	123.800
Georgetown Ground	124.500

Figure 12.2 Frequencies used en-route.

INTRODUCTION.

This flight scenario chapter is designed to put the RT phraseology and procedures that you have learned in this book into the context of a cross-country training flight by the pilot of a light aircraft, conducted in accordance with the Visual Flight Rules (VFR).

Because the flight takes place in lower airspace (typically, a light aircraft cross-country flight, over land, would be below 5 000 feet, above mean sea-level), the "radio environment" is one in which all radio frequencies are spaced at 25 Kilohertz (kHz).

As it is assumed that the flight takes place in Europe, all radio frequencies pronounced by controllers, ground station radio operators and the pilot are given either as four-digit frequencies (e.g. 123.8 MHz) or six-digit frequencies (e.g. 125.325 MHz), in accordance with the latest European regulations. Refer to Chapter 1, VHF Voice Communications, if you wish to remind yourself about the recent changes in RT phraseology, in terms of the transmission of VHF voice-communication frequencies.

If you fly outside Europe, where five-digit frequency pronunciation is still used, all you need to remember is that where you see a six-digit frequency in the flight scenario, you need to pronounce only the first five digits.

The flight scenario depicts a PA-28 carrying out a VFR cross-country flight from Walden to Georgetown, as depicted in *Figure 12.1*. The fictitious airspace on the chart in *Figure 12.1* is that used by the International Civil Aviation Organisation (ICAO) in its Manual of Radiotelephony, Doc 9432. We are grateful for ICAO's permission to use this fictitious chart.

The route of the cross-country flight passes under Airway Alpha 1 to the first turning point over the village of Cheame. From Cheame, the route continues westwards on its second leg, passing through the Stephenville Control Zone (CTR) to the second turning point at the village of Fordinghouse. The final leg of the route is in a southerly direction towards the destination aerodrome of Georgetown.

Both Walden and Georgetown have an Air Traffic Control Unit (ATCU), providing a full air traffic control service.

Clearly, if it were the pilot's principal aim simply to fly from Walden to Georgetown, he would take the direct route, on which, if the flight were VFR, little radio work would be involved. But the following flight scenario is a training cross-country flight, and so a route consisting of three legs has been planned.

The radio transmissions depicted in the flight scenario follow ICAO guidelines and may not always reflect exactly what you are used to hearing in the country in which you normally fly. However, though different countries have retained national variations in certain types of RT phraseology, the words and speech groups used in the RT transmissions in this scenario follow an ICAO format which is recognised and used by air traffic services, worldwide.

Any differences between ICAO RT phraseology and RT phraseology used in British airspace will be explained in the text. (An exclusively United Kingdom flight scenario is depicted in Chapter 14.)

The two radios depicted in the illustrations are 25 kHz-spaced radios, one with a 5-digit, single-frequency display and one with a 6-digit, single-frequency display. Most pilots flying light aircraft, VFR, in lower airspace, still use 5-digit radios. However, some 25 kHz radios are six-digit, so we depict both types in the diagrams.

A list of RT frequencies used during the flight scenario is given in *Figure 12.2*. Before departing on an actual cross-country flight, a pilot will identify all the frequencies that he will require during the flight, and enter them into his flight log.

The scenario begins with the PA-28 on the ground at Walden. The pilot has started the engine and is preparing to taxi.

The frequency that the pilot first selects is the Walden Automatic Terminal Information Service (ATIS) frequency of 121.750

Figure 12.3 On the ground at Walden, with the Walden ATIS frequency of 121.750 selected.

 This is Walden Information Mike timed at 1420Z. Runway 20, Right hand circuit. Surface wind 210°, 20 kts. 10 kilometres in haze. Cloud broken at 2500ft. Outside air temperature +7°, Dewpoint +6°, QNH 984 hectopascal*. On initial contact with Air Traffic Control confirm the QNH and information Mike received.

After noting all the relevant details from the ATIS broadcast, the pilot selects the Walden Ground frequency of 121.950 and calls GROUND.

 Walden Ground, G-FHJM, Request radio check, 121.950, and taxi for VFR flight to Georgetown, as notified, 3 persons on board, Information Mike received, QNH 984 hectopascal.

*   *N.B. The 'hectopascal' is used in many European countries as the unit of pressure for altimeter settings. In other countries, the 'millibar' remains in use. The units 'hectopascal' and 'millibar' are of the same value. Thus, an altimeter setting is numerically the same, whether given in 'hectopascal' or 'millibars'. The USA gives altimeter pressure settings in inches of Mercury (Hg). 1013 hectopascal or millibars is equal to 29.92 inches Hg. Hectopascal is used here as it is a fictitious scenario in following ICAO guidelines. For pressure readings greater than 1000 hectopascal/millibars, the units are omitted entirely.*

G-JM, Walden Ground, Read you 5, Taxi Holding Point Runway 20, QNH 984 hectopascal.

Readability 5, Taxi Holding Point Runway 20, QNH 984 hectopascal, G-JM.

Figure 12.4 At the holding point, Runway 20, Walden.

The pilot is now at the holding point for Runway 20. He has completed his power and pre-take off checks, and Walden Ground now instructs him to contact Walden Tower on 118.750.

G-JM, Contact Walden Tower, 118.750.

118.750, G-JM.

The pilot makes the change and listens out for a few seconds on 118.750, before transmitting, to ensure that no other RT exchange is currently in progress.

Walden Tower, G-FHJM, Ready for departure.

G-JM, Walden Tower, Line Up, Runway 20.

Lining up, Runway 20, G-JM.

G-JM, Runway 20, Cleared for take off, wind 210 degrees, 10 kts.

Cleared for take off, Runway 20, G-JM.

G-JM, Contact Walden Approach, 125.325.

125.325, G-JM.

Walden Approach, G-FHJM, Setting heading 033, Climbing to 2 500ft, QNH 984 hectopascal.

G-JM, Roger, Report reaching control zone boundary.

Wilco, G-JM.

G-JM, At control zone boundary, 2 500ft, QNH 984 hectopascale.

G-JM, Roger, Call when leaving the frequency.

Wilco, G-JM.

When he is some 10 miles from Walden, the pilot decides that he would like to get a Flight Information Service from Kennington.

 Walden Approach, G-JM, Changing to Kennington Approach, 128.950.

 G-JM, Roger, 128.950.

 Kennington Approach, G-FHJM, Request Flight Information Service.

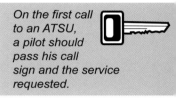
On the first call to an ATSU, a pilot should pass his call sign and the service requested.

 G-FHJM, Kennington Approach, Go ahead. *

Figure 12.5 At about 10 miles North of Walden, the pilot decides to request a Flight Information Service from Kennington on its approach frequency of 128.950.

* *Note: In the United Kingdom, the words, **"Pass your message"**, are used by controllers.*

G-FHJM, PA28, From Walden to Georgetown via Cheame and Fordinghouse, 10 miles North of Walden, at 2 500 feet on QNH 984 hectopascal, VFR, Estimate Cheame 07.

G-JM, Roger, Flight Information Service, QNH 986 hectopascal.

Flight Information Service, QNH 986 hectopascal, G-JM.

As you approach Cheame, the pilot decides to tell Kennington where he is.

Kennington Approach, G-JM, Overhead Cheame, Setting heading 263, 2 500 feet, QNH 986 hectopascal.

G-JM, Roger.

** *Note: In the United Kingdom, a pilot would be given the Regional Pressure Setting rather than an airfield QNH.* (See Volume 1: **Air Law**; Volume 3: **Navigation**; and Volume 4: **Meteorology**). *Also, in the United Kingdom, the controller would add the words "millibars" to a pressure reading of less than 1000 millibars (hectopascal).*

After some distance along the second leg, the Kennington controller may decide that he can no longer offer the pilot a Flight Information Service. There may be several reasons for this, such as the controller's workload or because the pilot is getting too far away to maintain good radio contact. Whatever the reason, the Kennington controller may ask the pilot to request a Flight Information Service from another ATSU, or from the Flight Information Region in which the route is being flown.

G-JM, Contact Alexander Information on 125.750 for further service.

125.750, G-JM.

Alexander Information is the Flight Information Service call-sign of the fictional Alexander Flight Information Region. All airspace is divided into Flight Information Regions (FIRs). One of the services offered by an FIR is a Flight Information Service. (See Volume 1: Air Law).

Figure 12.6 On the second leg of the route, receiving a Flight Information Service from Alexander Information.

The pilot changes to Alexander Information on 125.750.

Alexander Information, G-FHJM, Request Flight Information Service.

G-JM, Alexander Information, Go ahead. *

G-FHJM, PA28 from Walden to Georgetown via Cheame and Fordinghouse, 20 miles East of Stephenville, 2 500 feet, QNH 986 hectopascale, VFR, Estimate Stephenville 32.

As mentioned in Chapter 5, when receiving a Flight Information Service (FIS), a pilot may not get any information passed to him at all, unless he makes a specific request for information such as serviceability states of aerodromes on the route, frequencies, activity state of parachute dropping zones, etc. However, a pilot may be passed information relevant to his flight, and, in any case, when a pilot is receiving an FIS, he is at least in contact with an Air Traffic Service Unit (ATSU) which knows he is airborne and what his intended route is. This is a good situation to be in, should a pilot ever require specific help.

G-JM, Roger, Flight Information Service. Will you be crossing the Stephenville Control Zone?

Affirm, G-JM.

* Note: In the United Kingdom, a pilot would be requested to: **"Pass your message"**.

G-JM, Stephenville QNH 987 hectopascal.

Stephenville QNH 987 hectopascal, G-JM.

As the pilot approaches 10 miles from Stephenville Control Zone he will need to inform Alexander Information that he intends to change frequency to Stephenville Radar, which is the initial contact frequency for Stephenville Control Zone.

Alexander Information, G-JM, 10 miles East of Stephenville, Changing to Stephenville Radar, 128.150.

G-JM, Roger, 128.150.

The pilot now selects the Stephenville Radar frequency of 128.150.

Figure 12.7 Contacting Stephenville Radar on 128.150 to request control zone transit.

Stephenville Radar, G-FHJM, Request control zone transit.

G-FHJM, Stephenville Radar, Go ahead. *

G-FHJM, PA28 from Walden to Georgetown via Cheame and Fordinghouse, 10 miles East of Stephenville, 2000 feet, QNH 987 hectopascal, VFR, Estimate control zone boundary at 27.

G-JM, Roger, Squawk 6412.

Squawk 6412, G-JM.

G-JM, You are identified 8 miles East of Stephenville, Climb to 2 500 feet, QNH 987 hectopascal, Report level.

Climb to 2 500 feet QNH 987 hectopascal, Wilco, G-JM.

G-JM, Maintaining 2 500ft, QNH 987 hectopascal.

G-JM, Roger, Report reaching control zone boundary.

Wilco, G-JM.

The pilot is now approaching the edge of the Stephenville Control Zone (CTR) and he must call Stephenville Radar as instructed. Note that the pilot does not yet have positive clearance to enter the CTR, so he must make his call in sufficient time for the controller to give him that clearance before he actually reaches the edge of the CTR. If a pilot waits until he is at the CTR boundary before calling, he will almost certainly infringe the zone illegally.

*   *Note: In the United Kingdom, "Pass your message" would be used instead of "Go Ahead".*

Stephenville Radar, G-JM, Approaching the control zone boundary.

G-JM, Roger, Cleared to enter the Control Zone on present track, Maintain 2 500 feet, QNH 987 hectopascal.

Cleared to enter the Control Zone on present track, Maintain 2 500 feet, QNH 987 hectopascal, G-JM.

G-JM, Call when leaving the Control Zone.

Wilco, G-JM.

As the pilot approaches the CTR boundary:

G-JM, Leaving the Control Zone to the West, Heading 265.

G-JM, Roger, Squawk 7000, Call when leaving the frequency.

Squawk 7000, Wilco, G-JM.

Now that he has left the CTR, the pilot decides that he would like to receive a Flight Information Service (FIS), again. He could obtain an FIS from Stephenville but the pilot suspects they may be fairly busy, so he decides to change back to the Alexander Information frequency.

Figure 12.8 Leaving Stephenville CTR, squawking 7000.

G-JM, Changing to Alexander Information, 125.750.

Roger, 125.750.

Alexander Information, G-FHJM, Request Flight Information Service.

G-JM, Alexander Information, Go ahead. *

G-FHJM, PA28 from Walden to Georgetown, via Cheame and Fordinghouse, 7 miles West of Stephenville, 2 500 feet, QNH 987 hectopascal, VFR, Estimate Fordinghouse, 39.

G-JM, Roger, Flight Information Service.

Some time later, overhead the second turning point.

Alexander Information, G-JM, Fordinghouse, Setting heading 175 and descending to 2 000 feet to maintain VMC.

*   *Note: In the United Kingdom, "Pass your message" would be used instead of "Go Ahead".*

Figure 12.9 Overhead the second turning point, Fordinghouse.

G-JM, Roger.

Having begun the final leg, the pilot will need to give Georgetown sufficient warning that he wishes not only to enter their CTR but also to land. The pilot would call Georgetown on its initial contact frequency, which we will assume is the approach frequency, 120.625. We will also assume that the pilot has listened to the Georgetown ATIS which is giving Information HOTEL.

Alexander Information, G-JM, Changing to Georgetown Approach on 120.625.

G-JM, Roger, 120.625.

Georgetown Approach, G-FHJM, Request zone entry and joining instructions.

G-FHJM, Georgetown Approach, Go Ahead *.

*   Note: In the United Kingdom, "Pass your message" would be used instead of "Go Ahead".

G-FHJM, PA28, From Walden to Georgetown, 2 000 feet, QNH 987 hectopascal, 8 miles North of Georgetown, Estimate zone boundary at 55, Information Hotel.

G-JM, Roger, Georgetown QNH 988 hectopascal, enter the control zone from the North, report airfield in sight.

QNH 988 hectopascal, Wilco, G-JM.

Figure 12.10 On Georgetown approach frequency with Georgetown in sight.

The airfield is now in sight.

G-JM, At control zone boundary, Airfield in sight.

G-JM, Roger, Contact Tower, 123.8.

123.8, G-JM.

Georgetown Tower, G-FHJM.

G-JM, Tower, Join right base, Runway 23, QNH 988 hectopascal, Report final.

Join right base, Runway 23, QNH 988 hectopascal, Report final, G-JM.

Figure 12.11 At Georgetown, on the Tower frequency of 123.8, final approach.

The pilot is now on final.

G-JM, Final, Runway 23.

G-JM, Wind 220 degrees, 15 knots, Runway 23, Cleared to land.

Cleared to land, Runway 23, G-JM.

The aircraft is now on the ground.

G-JM, Take next exit left, When vacated contact Ground, 124.5.

Next left, When vacated, Ground, 124.5, G-JM.

G-JM, Runway vacated, Changing to Ground, 124.5.

G-JM, Roger.

Georgetown Ground, G-FHJM, Request taxi instructions.

G-JM, Georgetown Ground, Take next left and follow Taxiway Hotel to the end, Then right into Apron Delta.

Next left and follow Taxiway Hotel to the end, Then right into Apron Delta, G-JM.

G-JM, At Apron Delta, Shutting down.

G-JM, Roger.

SCENARIO ENDS

CHAPTER 13
UNITED KINGDOM DIFFERENCES IN RADIOTELEPHONY PHRASEOLOGY & PROCEDURES

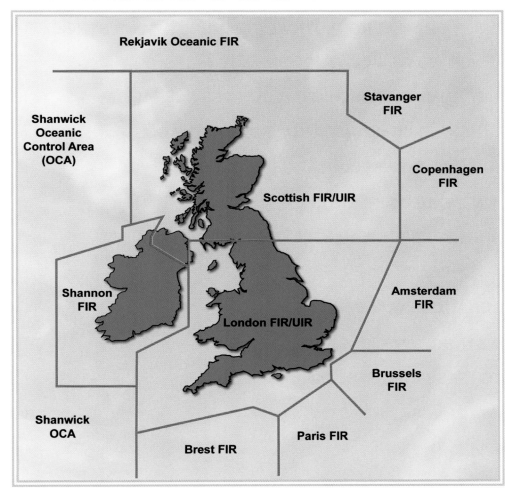

CHAPTER CONTENTS

INTRODUCTION   160

SUMMARY OF UK AND ICAO RT DIFFERENCES   160

GENERAL OPERATING PROCEDURES   163

CATEGORIES OF UK AERONAUTICAL COMMUNICATIONS SERVICE 164

THE FULL AIR TRAFFIC CONTROL SERVICE   165

THE AERODROME FLIGHT INFORMATION SERVICE (AFIS)   165

THE AIR-GROUND COMMUNICATIONS SERVICE (AGCS)   167

AFIS AND AGCS PHRASEOLOGY   168

RT AT UNATTENDED AIRFIELDS   176

THE STANDARD OVERHEAD JOIN   178

MANDATORY READBACK   178

CONDITIONAL CLEARANCES   179

LEVEL INSTRUCTIONS   179

REPLY TO "PASS YOUR MESSAGE"   181

CROSSING DANGER AREAS   182

SPECIAL VFR   185

VHF DIRECTION FINDING (VDF)   186

VDF IN AN EMERGENCY   188

THE SPEECHLESS CODE   191

MILITARY AERODROME TRAFFIC ZONES (MATZ)   192

LOWER AIRSPACE RADAR SERVICE   195

AIR TRAFFIC SERVICES OUTSIDE CONTROLLED AIRSPACE   196

HOW DO I ASK FOR A PARTICULAR SERVICE   197

INTRODUCTION

This chapter deals with the few significant differences between standard ICAO Radiotelephony (RT) phraseology and procedures, and RT in the United Kingdom.

The United Kingdom Civil Aviation Authority Radiotelephony (UK CAA) Manual, CAP 413, lays down the RT procedures, phraseology and techniques to be used in United Kingdom airspace. CAP 413 is based on the International Standards and Recommended Practices contained in ICAO Annex 10 Volume 2, and PANS ATM, Document 4444. These documents form the basis of the ICAO Manual of Radio Telephony upon which the JAR-FCL Syllabus and the previous chapters of this book are based.

While CAP 413 is almost identical to the ICAO Manual of Radiotelephony, there are several areas where RT procedures and phraseology in the United Kingdom (UK) differ from those recommended by ICAO. The differences mark those areas of RT phraseology and procedures where the ICAO standard may be misunderstood, or possesses certain weaknesses in the UK environment. This chapter is intended to highlight those differences.

The ICAO RT practices covered in Chapters 1 to 12 of this book lay down the fundamentals of VFR RT practice to be used by all ICAO member states.

The small number of differences in United Kingdom RT practices do not negate fundamental ICAO RT practices but rather adapt a small number of those practices to United Kingdom requirements.

United Kingdom based VFR pilots should note and use the UK differences when flying in United Kingdom airspace.

Students preparing for JAA/EASA PPL VFR RT (Communications) theoretical knowledge examinations set by the United Kingdom Civil Aviation Authority, or who are about to take the UK CAA Flight Radiotelephony Operator's Licence (FRTOL) test, must learn the UK RT differences and to apply them to examination and test questions*. However, examination candidates must always bear in mind that examination and test syllabuses are under the control of the national aviation authority. Consequently, before taking a test or examination, candidates should ensure that they are familiar with national aviation authority syllabuses or special requirements.

* The questions at the end of this book are aimed at helping readers to prepare for the PPL VFR Communications examination and FRTOL test set in the United Kingdom.

SUMMARY OF DIFFERENCES BETWEEN UK AND ICAO RT PHRASEOLOGY AND PROCEDURES

We begin by summarising, in tabular format, the most significant differences between UK and ICAO RT phraseology and procedures which affect the VFR pilot, and then expand on the principal differences.

The following "differences" table is an extract from the United Kingdom CAA Radiotelephony Manual, CAP 413.

Details of ICAO/UK Difference	Reason/Remarks
Phraseology **FLIGHT LEVEL ONE ZERO ZERO** (ICAO) is not used in **UK**. In the **UK** flight levels ending in hundreds are transmitted as **HUNDRED e.g. FLIGHT LEVEL ONE HUNDRED**.	To avoid potential confusion with adjacent flight levels and mis-identification of cleared levels e.g. FLIGHT LEVEL ONE ZERO ZERO with FLIGHT LEVEL ONE ONE ZERO.
In the **UK CONTACT** shall have the meaning **"Establish communications with... (your details have been passed)"**.	This shortens a pilot's first call on the next ATS unit/frequency, as he knows he does not have to pass full details.
In the **UK** the additional term - **FREECALL** shall have the meaning **"CALL (unit) (your details have not been passed)"**.	This informs the pilot that he will have to pass full details to the next ATS unit/frequency on first contact.
The phrase **GO AHEAD** (ICAO) is not used in the **UK**. In the **UK** the term **PASS YOUR MESSAGE** is used.	**GO AHEAD** is not used on safety grounds (e.g. to reduce runway incursions) where some pilots/drivers might confuse **GO AHEAD** with **PROCEED**.
RECLEARED (ICAO) is not used in **UK**.	The direction of vertical movement, provided by **CLIMB** and **DESCEND**, acts as a check in some circumstances when a pilot misinterprets a call not directed at him.
The following method of acknowledging receipt is not used in **UK**. **'The call-sign of the aircraft followed if necessary by call-sign of the aeronautical station'** (ICAO). **(CALL-SIGN) ROGER** is used in the UK.	The **UK** procedure is in accordance with the examples in ICAO Doc 9432 (1990) Manual of Radiotelephony, which are different to those described in ICAO Annex 10 Aeronautical Telecommunications.
NEGATIVE I SAY AGAIN (ICAO) is not used in the **UK**. In the **UK**, if a readback is incorrect, the aeronautical station shall transmit the word **NEGATIVE** followed by the correct version.	The phrase **I SAY AGAIN** is considered superfluous in this case.
The ICAO phraseology for conditional line-up clearance **FASTAIR 345, BEHIND THE DC9 ON SHORT FINAL, LINE UP BEHIND** (ICAO) is not used. In the **UK** the phrase **FASTAIR 345 AFTER THE LANDING DC9 LINE UP** is used.	AFTER is used instead of BEHIND to describe more clearly 'sequential following' rather than 'further back'. The reiteration of the condition at the end of the phrase is considered to reduce the clarity of the instruction.
In the **UK**, an additional phrase, **LAND AFTER THE (Aircraft Type)** is used.	This phrase may be used under certain conditions and indicates that a preceding aircraft is not clear of the runway.
In the **UK**, additional phrases, **LAND AT YOUR DISCRETION** and **TAKE-OFF AT YOUR DISCRETION** are used.	These phrases may be used under certain conditions and indicate that a landing clearance or a take-off clearance cannot be issued and any landing or take-off is to be conducted at the pilot's discretion.

Radiotelephony Reply Procedure In the **UK** under certain circumstances the answering ground station may omit its call-sign.	Omitting the ground station call-sign may reduce RTF congestion and therefore improve safety standards at busy ATC units.
Inter pilot air-to-air communication on 123.450 MHz. Air-to-air communications on frequency 123.450 MHz (ICAO) are not permitted in the **UK**.	Frequency 123.450 MHz is assigned for discrete ATC purposes within the **UK**.
Helicopter Phraseology Additional radiotelephony terms for helicopter operations are defined for use in the UK.	To reduce the possibility of misunderstanding, several additional terms pertaining to rotary wing operations are defined for use in the UK.
Listening Watch on 121.5 MHz ICAO Requirements for Aeronautical Station Listening Watch on the **VHF** emergency channel **121.5 MHz** are not applied in **UK**.	The **VHF** emergency channel frequency **121.5 MHz** is not routinely monitored at civil aerodromes, however, it is monitored 24 hours a day at Area Control Centres with coverage over most of the **UK** above 3000' amsl.
Atmospheric Pressure The term **HECTOPASCAL** is not used in the **UK**.	When describing atmospheric pressure, the term **MILLIBAR** (Mb) is used in the **UK** in place of **HECTOPASCAL** (hPa) (One Millibar being equal to one Hectopascal).

GENERAL OPERATING PROCEDURES

Hours of Service of Radio Facilities.

The hours of service of the radio facilities available in the United Kingdom are published in the En-Route and Aerodrome annexes of the UK Aeronautical Information Publication (AIP), sometimes referred to as the Air Pilot.

Maintaining a Listening Watch.

When an aircraft has established communication with an Air Traffic Service Unit (ATSU), the pilot is required to maintain a listening watch with that ATSU, and advise the unit when the listening watch is about to cease. Aircraft should not cease to maintain a listening watch, except for reasons of safety, without informing the ATSU concerned. The time at which it is expected that the watch will be resumed must also be stated. This means that whenever you change frequency and stop your listening watch, you must inform the ATSU whose frequency you are leaving.

Oxford Approach, G-FHJM, Changing to Luton Radar on 129.550.

G-JM, Oxford Approach, Roger.

CATEGORIES OF AERONAUTICAL COMMUNICATIONS SERVICE IN THE UNITED KINGDOM

In the United Kingdom, there are three main categories and levels of aeronautical communications service:

•   A full Air Traffic Control Service which is provided by licensed Air Traffic Control Officers who are closely regulated by the United Kingdom Civil Aviation Authority (UK CAA).

•   A Flight Information Service, known as a Basic service at some aerodromes, and on Flight Information Region FIS frequencies, is provided by licensed Flight Information Service Officers (FISOs) who are regulated by the UK CAA.

•   At small aerodromes, an Air/Ground Communications Service is provided by ground radio operators who are not licensed by the UK CAA, but who have obtained a certificate of competency from the UK CAA to operate ground radio equipment on aviation frequencies.

There are 3 categories of aeronautical communication service:
• Full air traffic control.
• Flight Information Service.
• Air-Ground Communications Service.

The qualifications of the operators providing each of the above levels of aeronautical communications service are very different. So, as you might expect, the level of service offered by each type of operator is very different, too.

The three types of aeronautical communications service mentioned above are provided throughout the world, regulated by national aviation authorities, in accordance ICAO guidelines. The fundamental difference between the three levels of service has been described in Chapter 4. That description included a detailed account of the full air traffic control service, as well as containing examples of the radiotelephony phraseology used between pilots and air traffic controllers in typical air and ground scenarios.

RT phraseology used between air traffic controllers and pilots is highly standardised throughout the world. Consequently, virtually all of Chapter 4 is relevant to RT in the United Kingdom. The few differences in air traffic control procedures and phraseology between UK and ICAO practices will be dealt with later in this chapter.

But the RT phraseology used by Aerodrome Flight Information Service Officers (AFISOs) and Air-Ground Communication Service Operators (AGCSOs) will differ greatly from country to country.

In this section, therefore, we will deal primarily with RT phraseology and procedures used, in the United Kingdom, between pilots and AFISOs, on the one hand, and pilots and AGCSOs, on the other.

The Full Air Traffic Control Service.

As you have learned, at larger aerodromes at which all air traffic movements are under the supervision and control of qualified air traffic controllers, full air traffic control is exercised by an Air Traffic Control Unit, (ATCU). The primary aim of ATCUs is preventing collisions between aircraft in the air and on the ground, and maintaining an orderly and expeditious flow of air traffic.

ATCUs operate on frequencies identified by such call-signs as GROUND, TOWER, APPROACH, RADAR, ZONE, etc. Air traffic controllers operating at these stations are responsible for controlling and issuing instructions and advice to aircraft taxying on the manoeuvring area, flying in, or in the immediate vicinity of, the aerodrome circuit, and those aircraft approaching the aerodrome from outside its zone boundaries, or aircraft having just departed from the zone.

Figure 13.1.

The full air traffic control service and associated RT procedures and phraseology are dealt with in Chapters 4 and 5.

The Aerodrome Flight Information Service in the United Kingdom.

Where a full air traffic service is not established at an aerodrome with an Aerodrome Traffic Zone (ATZ), the aerodrome may provide an Aerodrome Flight Information Service (AFIS) in order to pass to pilots information which will permit the safe and expeditious movement of air traffic within the ATZ.

The call-sign suffix of an aerodrome ground station which provides an AFIS is INFORMATION.

A pilot receiving an AFIS is not under air traffic control when airborne, or when on the runway engaged in landing or take-off manoeuvres. An Aerodrome Flight Information Service Officer (AFISO) may, however, issue instructions to the pilots of aircraft on the ground up to the holding point and, in the case of aircraft landing, after the landing roll is completed.

When receiving an AFIS, it remains the responsibility of the Pilot-in-Command of an aircraft, in flight, or during take-off and landing manoeuvres on the runway, to decide the appropriate course of action to be taken to ensure the safe conduct of his flight and the safety of his aircraft.

An AFISO in not able to issue clearances; it is, therefore, important that pilots understand that they should not request clearances from an AFISO.

The aim of the Aerodrome Flight Information Service is to pass to pilots information which will permit the safe and efficient contact of air traffic within an ATZ.

When a pilot, in flight, is receiving an Aerdrome Flight Information Service, he is not under air traffic control. But an AFISO may give instructions to the pilots of aircraft on the ground which are not engaged in take-off or landing manoeuvres.

The call-sign suffix of an aerodrome ground station which provides an Aerodrome Flight Information Service is **INFORMATION**.

AFISOs are permitted to pass instructions to helicopters engaged in air taxying. However, when a helicopter pilot reports ready to lift-off and depart, the AFISO will revert to passing information to the pilot. In the case of inbound helicopters, AFISOs pass information to the pilot until he has landed or transited to the hover, prior to air taxying to the parking area. Thereafter, an AFISO may pass instructions to the pilot until the helicopter lands.

AFISOs may issue taxi instructions. A Pilot-In-Command of an aircraft on the ground must contact the AFISO on watch, and request taxi instructions, before entering an aerodrome's manoeuvring area.

Where an AFIS is being provided at an aerodrome, the Pilot-In-Command of an aircraft is required to obtain the permission of the AFISO on watch, before moving on the apron and manoeuvring area. Pilots must contact the AFISO and request taxi instructions before entering the aerodrome's manoeuvring area.

An AFISO's area of responsibility is the aerodrome, the ATZ, and the immediate surrounding local area. An AFISO may pass traffic or essential aerodrome information to a pilot, in flight, who contacts the AFISO on the RT. But any traffic information passed should relate only to <u>known</u> traffic, operating, or intending to operate, within the AFISO's area of responsibility.

Figure 13.2.

AFISO Phraseology.

Certain types of RT phraseology are used between Aerodrome Flight Information Service Officers (AFISOs) and pilots, which identify, and are appropriate to, the AFISO's level of authority. The RT exchanges on Pages 164 to 172 illustrate this phraseology.

You should particularly note that at aerodromes providing an Aerodrome Flight Information Service (AFIS), the phrase 'at your discretion' is used, in RT phraseology relating to landing and take-off, to indicate that the AFISO is not issuing a clearance. Pilots should NOT respond to this phrase, using the words 'at my discretion' but should acknowledge in one of the following ways.

G-JM, Land at your discretion, Wind 220, 5 knots.

A pilot's reply to an AFISO's transmission "Land at your discretion" would be "Roger" or "Landing", followed by the aircraft's call-sign. Pilots may also use, simply, the aircraft's call-sign to acknowledge the transmission.

Roger, G-JM.

<u>or</u>

Landing, G-JM.   <u>or</u>   **G-JM.**

Similarly:

G-JM, Take-off at your discretion, Wind 190, 15 knots.

Roger, G-JM.

or

 Taking off, G-JM. **or** **G-JM.**

The Air-Ground Communications Service in the United Kingdom.

Where an aerodrome has neither a full Air Traffic Control Service nor an Aerodrome Flight Information Service (AFIS), for instance at small airfields from which light aircraft only operate, an Air-Ground Communications Service (AGCS) may be available.

An AGCS Station is the simplest form of aeronautical radio communication service.

The AGCS operator is not trained to the same level as an AFISO, nor is he able to exercise the competencies of an AFISO.

An AGCS radio operator is not permitted to give any air traffic instructions or clearances to aircraft in the air or on the ground, though he may relay instructions and clearances given by a controller.

An AGCS facility permits two way communications between an aircraft and a ground station in which the AGCS operator may pass only very basic, advisory information regarding the situation at the aerodrome. The service is provided by radio operators who are not licensed but have obtained a certificate of competency from the UK CAA.

The call-sign suffix of an aerodrome ground station which provides an AGCS is RADIO.

An Air Ground Communications Service (AGCS) is competent to provide basic aerodrome and traffic information only. Pilots should note that, in some instances, the AGCS station may even be situated in a location from which the radio operator has no view, or only a restricted view, of the aerodrome.

As is the case with AFISOs, a certain type of RT phraseology is used between Air Ground Communications Service (AGCS) operators and pilots which identifies and is appropriate to the AGCS operator's level of competence. The RT exchanges on Pages 168 to 176 illustrate this phraseology.

An Air - Ground Communications Service Operator is not permitted to give air traffic instructions or clearances to aircraft in the air or on the ground.

*The call-sign suffix of an aerodrome ground station which provides an Air - Ground Communications Service is **RADIO**.*

Figure 13.3 An Air-Ground Communications Service Operator.

You should note especially, that AGCS operators must <u>not</u> use the expression: 'At your discretion'. The AGCS operator may pass <u>information only</u> to a pilot such as the runway-in-use, advisory QFEs or QNHs, wind velocity and details of any known traffic operating in the circuit area or in the ATZ, if the airfield possesses an ATZ.

Pilots must not request clearances or instructions from an AGCS operator, as no clearances or instructions may be given by the AGCS operator.

Examples of AFISO and AGCSO Phraseology.

The following examples of RT exchanges between pilots and Aerodrome Flight Information Service Officers (AFISOs), on the one hand, and pilots and Air Ground Communications Service Operators (AGCSOs), on the other, illustrate the differences between the competencies of the AFISO and AGCSO discussed above.

The RT exchanges which follow should allow you to see the differences between AFISO and AGCSO phraseology; but do bear in mind that the examples given do not represent the complete exchange of RT calls that might occur in each situation.

Situation 1 - Aircraft ready to taxi:

AFISO.

Barnchester Information, G-FHJM, By the fuel pumps, VFR to Seaton, Request taxi instructions.

G-JM, Taxi holding point Runway 23, Left Hand Circuit, QNH 1010, Surface Wind 220 degrees 12 kts.

Taxi to holding point Runway 23, QNH 1010, G-JM.

Air-Ground Operator.

Oakton Radio, G-ABCD, Radio check, 123.0, Request taxi information.

G-CD, Oakton Radio, Readability 5, Runway 02, Right hand circuit, Advisory QNH 1008.

Runway 02, Advisory QNH 1008, G-CD.

Situation 2 - Crossing a runway:

AFISO.

G-JM, At holding point Runway 31, Request cross runway.

G-JM, Cross runway 31, Report vacated.

Crossing Runway 31, Wilco, G-JM.

Air-Ground Operator.

G-CD, Crossing Runway 27 at threshold.

G-CD, No reported traffic.

Situation 3 - Aircraft Ready for Departure:

AFISO.

G-JM, Ready for departure.

G-JM, Hold position.

Holding, G-JM.

Air-Ground Operator.

G-ABCD, Ready for departure.

G-CD, Traffic is a PA-28 on base leg.

Roger, Holding, G-CD.

AFISO.

G-JM, Ready for departure.

G-JM, Traffic is a PA-28, Base leg, Report entering the runway and lining up.

Holding, Wilco, G-JM.

G-JM, Entering Runway 23, Lining up.

G-JM, Take off at your discretion, Surface Wind 220, 8 knots.

Taking off, G-JM.

Air-Ground Operator.

G-CD, Ready for departure.

G-CD, Roger, Traffic is a Cessna 152, 3 miles final, Surface Wind 350, 15 knots.

Taking off, G-CD.

AFISO.

G-JM, Ready for departure.

G-JM, No reported traffic, Surface Wind 220, 10 knots, Take off at your discretion.

Taking off, G-JM.

Air-Ground Operator.

G-CD, Ready for departure.

G-CD, No reported traffic, Wind 350, 12 knots.

Roger, Taking off, G-CD.

Situation 4 - When Airborne:

AFISO.

G-JM, Leaving the circuit to the North, Will contact you again when rejoining

G-JM, Roger.

Air-Ground Operator.

G-CD, Leaving circuit to the West, Will contact you again when rejoining.

G-CD, Roger.

Situation 5 - Aircraft Wishing to Transit the ATZ:

Pilots are required to report entering or leaving an Air Traffic Zone. AFISOs may request pilots to report at specific positions. These requests are not instructions, though most pilots will comply with the request. Air to Ground Operators, on the other hand, may only pass aerodrome information.

AFISO.

Barnchester Information, G-FHJM, Request transit your ATZ at 2000 ft.

G-FHJM, Barnchester Information, Pass your message.

G-FHJM, PA-28 from Rissington Magna to Netherford, 5 miles West of your ATZ, 2000 ft, on Cotswold 1008, Estimate ATZ boundary 35.

G-JM, Roger, Runway 23 in use, Left Hand, QNH 1010, Two aircraft in the circuit, Report entering ATZ.

Roger, QNH 1010, Wilco, G-JM.

Air-Ground Operator.

Oakton Radio, G-ABCD, Request traffic information.

G-ABCD, Oakton Radio, Pass your message.

G-ABCD, Cessna 152, From Shipton to Netherford, 5 miles South of your ATZ, 2000 ft on Cotswold 1008, Estimate overhead Oakton 15.

G-CD, Roger, Runway-in-use 02, Powered traffic left hand, Gliders right hand operating up to the ceiling of the ATZ, One PA-28 joining from the North, Advisory QNH 1010.

QNH 1010, Will report overhead, at 2500 feet, G-CD.

G-CD, Overhead at time 18, Will report leaving your frequency.

G-CD, Roger.

Situation 6 - Aircraft wishes to enter an ATZ for landing:

AFISO.

Barnchester Information, G-FHJM, PA-28, 15 miles South, 2500 ft, Regional Pressure Setting 1008, Request landing information.

G-JM, Barnchester Information, Runway 23 left hand, QNH 1010, Surface wind 225 degrees 12 kts. Traffic information, One Cessna on base leg and 2 Warriors downwind. Caution grass cutting to the North of Runway 23, Report Overhead.

Roger, Runway 23 left hand, QNH 1010, Wilco, G-JM.

Air-Ground Operator.

Oakton Radio, G-ABCD, Cessna 152, 5 miles South, 2500 ft, Regional Pressure Setting 1008, Request landing information.

G-CD, Oakton Radio, Runway 02, Right hand, Advisory QNH 998 millibars, No reported traffic, standard join is downwind.

Roger, Runway 02, right hand, Advisory QNH 998, Will join downwind, G-CD.

AFISO.

G-JM, Overhead, Descending dead side, Runway 23.

G-JM, Roger, One Cessna downwind and one Warrior on final, Report final.

Wilco, G-JM.

G-JM, Final.

G-JM, Land at your discretion, Surface wind 220 degrees 10 kts.

> At an aerodrome with an Aerodrome Flight Information Service, when the pilot of G-XY, on final, receives the transmission "G-XY, Land at your discretion", the correct reply from the pilot is either "G-XY", "Roger, G-XY" or "Landing, G-XY".

Landing, G-JM.

Air-Ground Operator.

G-CD, Downwind, Runway 02 right hand.

G-CD, No reported circuit traffic.

G-CD, Final.

G-CD, Surface wind 350 degrees, 5 kts.

Landing, G-CD.

Situation 7 - Aircraft reports landed and runway vacated:
AFISO.

G-JM, Runway vacated.

G-JM, Roger, Follow the Jodel D-140, Taxi along Runway 05 to the flying club.

After the Jodel D-140, Taxi along Runway 05 to the flying club, G-JM.

Air-Ground Operator.

G-CD, Runway vacated, Taxying to the flying club.

G-CD, Roger, No reported traffic.

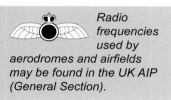

Radio frequencies used by aerodromes and airfields may be found in the UK AIP (General Section).

RADIOTELEPHONY AT UNATTENDED AERODROMES IN THE UNITED KINGDOM

Radio frequencies used by licensed aerodromes and airfields may be found in the United Kingdom Aeronautical Information Publication, (General Section).

However, pilots may find that they sometimes fly to, or operate from, aerodromes which have no allocated air-ground frequency. For operations at such aerodromes, sometimes referred to as unattended aerodromes, a common frequency, known as SAFETYCOM has been made available so that pilots can transmit their intentions to other aircraft which may be flying at, or in the vicinity of, the unattended aerodrome.

The **Safetycom Frequency** is **135.475 MHz**.

Pilots making transmissions on 135.475 MHz when operating at or near unattended aerodromes should address those transmissions to the aerodrome name followed by the suffix "Traffic". Pilots should not expect a reply to transmissions that they make on the Safetycom frequency.

At an unattended airfield, a standard overhead join allows the pilot to determine runway-in-use through observation of the windsock or signal square. But be sure to confirm that the airfield operating procedures permit an overhead join to be made.

Although unattended aerodrome transmissions are made at the discretion of the pilot, if transmissions on the Safetycom frequency are made, the pattern of the transmissions should conform to a standard pattern. Examples of Safetycom transmissions are given on the following page.

For more information on radiotelephony reports at unattended aerodromes, pilots should consult **CAP 413**.

The following RT transmissions illustrate the type of Safetycom transmissions that may be made when an aircraft is making a standard overhead join at an airfield. The standard overhead join is a suitable join to make at small airfields <u>if the airfield operating procedures permit it</u>, as the overhead join enables pilots to determine effectively the runway-in-use (through observation of the windsock and/or signal square) and the extent of any circuit traffic.

The use of 134.475 MHz does not confer any right of way on pilots using the frequency. The Rules of the Air must be complied with at all times, and pilots must not neglect to keep a vigilant lookout for other traffic.

CAP 413 lists the following additional points concerning the Safetycom frequency.

• Safetycom is not an Air Traffic Service and no aeronautical ground station is associated with Safetycom.

• Safetycom is a single common frequency and pilots should be aware of the possibility of congestion and breakthrough.

• It is particularly important when using Safetycom that RT transmissions identify the aerodrome name (suffixed 'traffic') in order to indicate the relevance of the report to other aircraft. Transmissions must be correct and concise.

• Safetycom transmissions shall only be made when aircraft are below 2000 ft above aerodrome level, or below 1000 ft above promulgated circuit height (if applicable), and within 10 nm of the aerodrome of intended landing.

Pilots should also note that where an unattended aerodrome lies within controlled airspace, pilots are to call the appropriate Air Traffic Control Unit in order to obtain a clearance to enter the controlled airspace.

Example of a Safetycom Transmission then Joining an Unattended Aerodrome.

Walthorpe Traffic, G-FHJM, 10 miles Southwest, Joining Overhead.

Walthorpe Traffic, G-FHJM, Overhead, Joining for Runway 20.

Walthorpe Traffic, G-FHJM, Dead side, Descending, Runway 20.

Walthorpe Traffic, G-FHJM, Downwind, Runway 20, To land.

Walthorpe Traffic, G-FHJM, Base Leg, Runway 20.

Walthorpe Traffic, G-FHJM, Final, Runway 20.

The Standard Overhead Join.

The following diagram illustrates how a typical standard overhead join is flown. This type of join is suitable for joining small airfields without air traffic control, if local procedures allow it. Always check first.

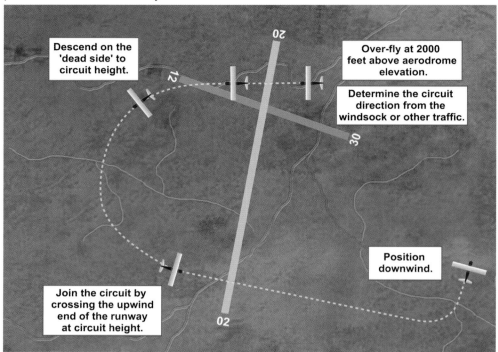

Figure 13.4 Standard Overhead Join for Runway 20.

MANDATORY READBACK

The full list of RT messages and clearances which must be read back in the United Kingdom is given below.

•   Taxi Instructions.

•   Level Instructions.

•   Heading Instructions.

•   Speed Instructions.

•   Airways or Route Clearances.

•   Approach Clearances.

•   Runway-in-Use.

•   Clearance to Enter, Land On, Take-Off On, Backtrack, Cross, or Hold Short of any Active Runway.

•   SSR (transponder) Operating Instructions.

•   Altimeter Settings.

•   Very High Frequency Direction Finding Information.

•   Frequency Changes.

•   Type of Radar Service.

•   Transition Levels.

CONDITIONAL CLEARANCES

In the United Kingdom, the format of the conditional clearance is shorter than in standard ICAO RT phraseology. An example of ICAO phraseology for a conditional clearance to line up would be:

Note that the format of the conditional clearance in the United Kingdom is slightly different from the ICAO format.

        G-CD, Behind the landing 757, Line up and wait, Behind.

In the United Kingdom, the conditional clearance would take the following form:

        G-CD, After the landing 757, Line up and wait.

LEVEL INSTRUCTIONS

When flying in United Kingdom airspace, the RT terminology associated with issuing and acknowledging level instructions is very similar to that given in the ICAO Manual of Radiotelephony. However, there are certain significant differences. In the United Kingdom, when passing level instructions, the following conventions apply:

•   The word 'to' is to be omitted from messages relating to FLIGHT LEVELS.

•   All messages relating to an aircraft's climb or descent to a HEIGHT or ALTITUDE employ the word 'to' followed immediately by the word HEIGHT or ALTITUDE. Furthermore, the initial message in any such RT exchange will also include the appropriate QFE or QNH.

In the United Kingdom, all messages relating to an aircraft's climb or descent to a HEIGHT or ALTITUDE should employ the word TO, followed immediately by the word HEIGHT or ALTITUDE.

The following examples illustrate how RT phraseology associated with level instructions is used in the United Kingdom.

The first examples deal only with FLIGHT LEVELS. Therefore, you should note that the word 'to' is missing.

        G-CD, Report your level.

Maintaining Flight Level 65, G-CD.

G-CD, Descend Flight Level 45.

Descend Flight Level 45, G-CD.

In the next example, the word 'to' is used when referring to HEIGHTS (based on an altimeter subscale setting of QFE) or ALTITUDES (based on an altimeter subscale setting of QNH).

G-JM, Report your level.

Maintaining altitude 2500 feet, Regional Pressure Setting 1006, G-JM.

G-JM, Descend to altitude 2000 feet, Walden QNH 1008.

Descend to altitude 2000 feet, Walden QNH 1008, G-JM.

G-JM, Descend to altitude 1500 feet.

Descend to altitude 1500 feet, G-JM.

G-JM, Descend to height 1000 feet, QFE 1005.

Descend to height 1000 feet, QFE 1005, G-JM.

Pilots are expected to comply with ATC level instructions as soon as they are issued. However, when a climb or descent is left to the discretion of the pilot, the words 'when ready' will be used; in these circumstances the pilot will report 'leaving' his present level.

REPLY TO 'PASS YOUR MESSAGE'

When first contacting an Air Traffic Service Unit, pilots should always request the service they require (e.g. Basic Service, Traffic Service, Deconfliction Service or Procedural Service.) In the United Kingdom, the response to a pilot's initial call will invariably be a request to 'Pass your message'. (Standard ICAO phraseology is "Go Ahead".)

The pilot's response to the instruction "Pass your message" should contain as much of the following information as possible.

A pilot should state the service he requires on initial contact with an Air Traffic Service Unit.

•   Aircraft Call-sign and Aircraft Type.

•   Departure Point and Destination.

•   Present Position.

•   Altitude or Level.

•   Additional Details and intentions (e.g. Flight Rules, Next Point on route).

The pilot should try to give all of the above information, and in the order shown, because the information will tell the controller where the pilot is, and what he intends to do. The controller will then be in a better position to give the pilot the service he requires, promptly and efficiently. The pilot should, therefore, learn the content and order of the reply to "Pass your message" thoroughly. Remember the rules of good RT, and do not begin to transmit information until you are sure of what you are going to say.

Learn thoroughly the order and content of the pilot's reply to the instruction, "Pass your message". The manner in which you reply to this instruction will tell the controller a great deal about your proficiency as a pilot/radio operator.

It is a particularly common mistake for pilots to be hesitant about their present position. Therefore, a pilot must be sure that he knows where he is, and how he is going to describe his position, before pressing the transmit button.

If you have done any flying in the United Kingdom already, you will no doubt have heard pilots passing information over the RT in a very long winded fashion, because they have not thought about what they were going to say before saying it. As a result, they block the radio for an unnecessarily long time and make everyone listening, including the controller, very frustrated. Do not fall into this trap yourself.

The following brief example illustrates how the reply to "Pass your message" should be made.

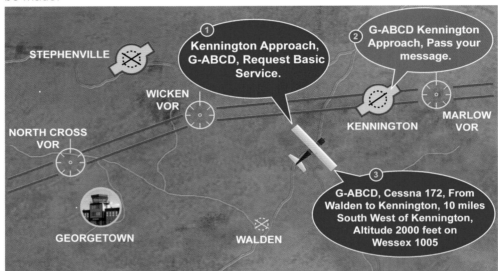

Figure 13.5 The reply to "Pass your message".

CROSSING DANGER AREAS

Danger Area Crossing Service (DACS).

A Danger Area Crossing Service (DACS) is available for approximately 24% of United Kingdom Danger Areas. Details of the DACS frequencies are found in the ENR section of the UK AIP and are also printed on the UK 1:500 000 UK ICAO Aeronautical Chart legend. *(See Figure 13.6.)*

Air Traffic Service Units (ATSUs) providing a DACS will, where appropriate, give a clearance for an aircraft to cross a Danger Area under a Traffic Service or a Basic Service. The clearance given relates only to the activity within the Danger Area. No separation from other traffic in the Danger Area is given.

 Kennington Approach, G-ABCD, Request Danger Area Crossing Service for Loudwater range.

 G-ABCD, Kennington Approach, Basic Service, Loudwater active, Report 10 miles from Loudwater.

 Danger Area Crossing Service, Wilco, G-ABCD.

Figure 13.6 Frequencies to contact for UK Danger Area Crossing Service and the Danger Area Activity Information Service may be found on the UK 1:500 000 Aeronautical Charts.

Kennington Approach, G-ABCD, 10 miles from Loudwater.

G-CD, Roger, Loudwater remains active, Suggest you re-route

Re-routing to the North of Loudwater and changing to Colinton Information 125.750, G-CD.

G-CD, Roger.

Kennington Approach, G-ABCD, 10 miles from Loudwater.

G-ABCD, Roger. Loudwater not active, Range crossing approved, Report vacating the range.

Range crossing approved, Wilco, G-ABCD.

Danger Area Activity Information Service (DAAIS).

Details of the frequencies to contact for this service are found in the ENR section of the UK AIP and are also printed on the UK 1:500 000 UK ICAO Aeronautical Charts legends. *(See Figure 13.6.)*

An Air Traffic Services Unit providing a Danger Area Activity Information Service cannot give a pilot a clearance to enter or cross a Danger Area.

It must be stressed that the Danger Area Activity Information Service (DAAIS) is purely an information service that will inform you whether or not a particular Danger Area is active. A DAAIS cannot give you clearance to enter or cross a Danger Area.

Details of the format of radio calls to be made when contacting a DAAIS are contained in the ENR section of the UK AIP.

With the Danger Area Activity Information Service, the nominated service unit will pass to the pilot, on request, an update on the known activity status of the Danger Area. This update will help the pilot to decide whether it is prudent, on flight safety grounds, to penetrate the Danger Area. The unit operating the Danger Area Activity Information Service does not issue clearances to cross Danger Areas. Such clearances are issued through the Danger Area Crossing Service.

Kennington Approach, G-ABCD, Request Danger Area Activity Information Service for Loudwater range.

G-ABCD, Kennington Approach, Loudwater range is active.

Loudwater active, G-ABCD.

Pilots should note that if no reply is received from an ATSU listed as providing a DACs or a DAAIS, it should be assumed that the Danger Area is active.

SPECIAL VFR (SVFR) IN THE UNITED KINGDOM

General.

A Special VFR (SVFR) flight is a VFR flight cleared by an Air Traffic Control Unit (ATCU) to operate within a Control Zone (CTR) where, in normal circumstances, an IFR clearance would be required.

It is implicit in the SVFR clearance that the pilot remains in sight of the surface and clear of cloud, at all times.

The rules concerning SVFR in the United Kingdom differ in some details from those stipulated by ICAO.

A special VFR clearance permits a pilot, without an Instrument Rating, to enter and fly within a CTR where normally an IFR clearance would be required.

Rules and Conditions Applying to the Special VFR Clearance in the UK.

An SVFR clearance may be requested without the submission of a filed flight plan and also whilst airborne. The pilot is required, however, to pass brief details of his flight to the appropriate Air Traffic Control Unit (ATCU). These details should include:

    a.   Aircraft call-sign.

    b.   Aircraft type.

    c.   Pilot's intentions.

    d.   Estimated time of arrival (ETA) at the **CTR** entry point.

You should note, however, that a full flight plan must be submitted if the pilot wishes the destination aerodrome to be notified of the SVFR flight.

When requesting a Special VFR clearance, over the radio, while airborne, the pilot should include in his request:

- *Aircraft call-sign.*

- *Aircraft type.*

- *Pilot's intentions.*

- *ETA at CTR entry point.*

The following general rules and conditions apply to SVFR:

- SVFR is limited to a VFR flight within a CTR when unable to comply with the Instrument Flight Rules.

- If the departure aerodrome is in the vicinity of the CTR wishing to be entered, a request for a SVFR clearance may be made by telephone.

- All requests for SVFR flights into a CTR made over the radio or by telephone must specify the estimated time of entry into the CTR. A request by radio must be made between 5 and 10 minutes before entering the CTR.

- Pilots should assume that the ATCU may not be able to assure separation from all other aircraft and must, therefore, maintain a good lookout.

- An SVFR clearance will be granted only when traffic conditions permit the flight to take place without hindrance to normal IFR flights.

- Generally, a fixed wing aircraft will not be cleared to depart a CTR under SVFR when the visibility is 1 800 metres or less, and/or the cloud ceiling is less than 600 feet.

- Under an SVFR clearance a VFR pilot is not allowed to fly in a CTR when the visibility is less than 10 kilometres.

- The pilot is to remain at all times in conditions which will enable him to determine his flight path in order to avoid obstacles.

- When operating in accordance with SVFR, the pilot must comply with ATC instructions.

- ATC may find it necessary to impose a height limitation on an SVFR flight.

- Pilots must not assume that an SVFR clearance into a CTR is a clearance into an ATZ within that CTR. Pilots will need to confirm with the appropriate Air Traffic Service Unit that they are, in fact, cleared into the ATZ concerned.

- **An SVFR clearance absolves the pilot from the 1 000 feet Low Flying Rule but none of the other Low Flying Rules.**

VHF DIRECTION FINDING

The aeronautical stations that offer a VHF Direction Finding (VDF) service are listed in the Communications section of the United Kingdom Aeronautical Information publication.

The QDM is the magnetic bearing from the aircraft to the VDF station. If there is no wind, the QDM will be the magnetic heading that the aircraft must steer to reach the station. If there is wind, a wind correction angle will have to be applied to the QDM to obtain the heading to steer.

Some stations stipulate that the service is not available for en-route navigation purposes (except in emergency). VDF bearing information will be given only when conditions are satisfactory, and when radio bearings fall within the calibrated limits of the station. If the provision of a radio bearing is not possible, the pilot will be told of the reason.

A pilot may request a bearing or heading using the appropriate phrase or Q code to specify the service required. When requested, a VDF station will provide an approximate bearing or heading and distance.

QDR	QDM	QTE
The magnetic bearing of the aircraft from the station.	The magnetic heading to be steered by the aircraft (assuming no wind) to reach the VDF station.	The true bearing of the aircraft from the station.

Figure 13.7 QDR, QDM and QTE.

The classes of bearing given by the ground station are shown in *Figure 13.8*. Because of equipment limitations, an accuracy of no better than 'Class B' should be expected.

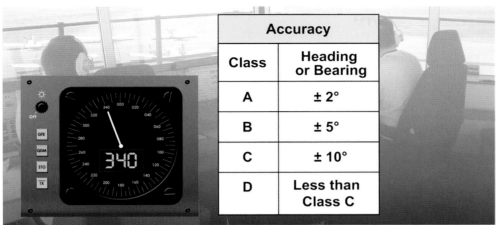

The limit of accuracy of Class B VDF bearing is ±5°.

Accuracy	
Class	Heading or Bearing
A	± 2°
B	± 5°
C	± 10°
D	Less than Class C

Figure 13.8 The class of accuracy of VDF bearings.

The correct phraseology for requesting a QDM from a VDF station is illustrated below.

The initial request for a VDF service is made as follows. Notice that the VDF service is referred to as Homing.

Steerton Approach, G-ABCD, request homing.

G-ABCD, Steerton Approach, Pass your message.

G-ABCD, Cessna 152, 15 miles West of Steerton, Heading 090, 2500 feet, Southwolds 995, Inbound to Steerton, Information Delta, Request Homing.

G-CD, Roger, Steerton QNH 998, QDM 085, Class Bravo.

Steerton QNH 998, QDM 085, Class Bravo, G-CD.

As the VDF service continues, the pilot requests a series of QDMs in order to home to the aerodrome at which the VDF station is located. **Notice that during the routine requests for a QDM, the pilot pronounces his aircraft's call-sign at both the beginning and end of his transmission.**

G-CD, Request QDM, G-CD.

G-CD, QDM 090.

QDM 090, G-CD.

When a pilot requests a QTE (true bearing) from the VDF station, he pronounces the words 'true bearing, true bearing' at the start of his transmission, in order to give the controller time to make the QTE selection on his VDF equipment before the transmission ends.

In the case of a request for a true bearing, it is normal for the controller to repeat the true bearing information.

True bearing, True bearing, Steerton Approach, G-ABCD, Request true bearing, G-ABCD.

G-ABCD, Steerton Approach, True bearing 325 degrees true, I say again, 325 degrees true, Class Bravo.

True bearing 325 degrees, Class Bravo, G-ABCD.

VHF DIRECTION FINDING IN AN EMERGENCY

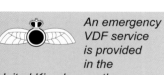

An emergency VDF service is provided in the United Kingdom on the international emergency frequency of 121.5 MHz.

In the United Kingdom, a pilot who is lost or uncertain of his position may be able to obtain direct help from the ground station with which he is in contact, or he may seek assistance, or be advised to seek assistance, from a Distress and Diversion (D&D) Cell on the international, aeronautical VHF distress frequency of 121.5 MHz.

There are two D&D Cells; one at Prestwick to serve the region North of Latitude 55° N, and one at West Drayton to serve the area South of 55° N. Although both D&D Cells are manned by Royal Air Force personnel, they provide a service to civil aircraft in an emergency, in addition to the service they provide to military aircraft. This includes the provision of a position fixing service.

The D&D Cells obtain information on the position of an aircraft in distress from VDF equipment, and are able to fix with good accuracy the position of aircraft transmitting on 121.5 MHz at altitudes of 3 000 feet, and above, over the United Kingdom land area and coastal waters. However, the ability to locate aircraft below **3 000 feet** is poor and will probably be severely inhibited over the mountainous areas of Scotland, Wales and North-West England.

The D&D service is available around the clock to pilots flying within United Kingdom airspace.

For aircraft flying in the London FIR, overland, South of the River Humber and East of Manchester, auto-triangulation position fixing is possible which can give the West Drayton D&D Cell an almost immediate fix on the position of an aircraft in distress. Within a radius of about 40 nautical miles of West Drayton, auto-triangulation position fixing is possible in respect of aircraft flying at 2 000 feet or above.

In other areas, bearing information has to be obtained by the D&D controller through telephone contact with other VDF-equipped aerodromes, and then plotted manually. In this second type of procedure, fixing the position of an aircraft in distress may take several minutes, as opposed to seconds with auto-triangulation.

Figure 13.9 depicts the approximate boundary of the area of the United Kingdom in which the West Drayton D&D Cell can carry out auto-triangulation position fixing. In the remaining area of the United Kingdom, manual plotting is required.

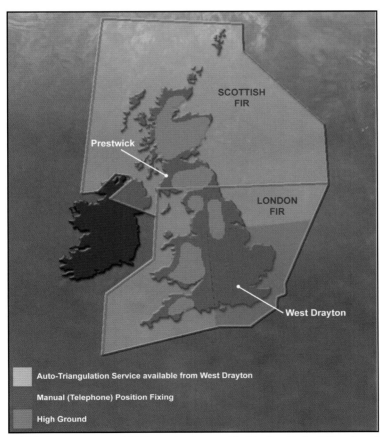

Figure 13.9 An emergency VDF service is provided in the United Kingdom by two Distress & Diversion Cells.

Pilots may simulate emergency situations, BUT NOT THE STATE OF DISTRESS, on 121.5 MHz, in order to enable them to gain experience of the service provided.

With both types of position-fixing procedures, the accuracy of the fix depends very much on the quality of the bearings, which in turn depends upon the height of the aircraft and its distance from the ground station.

Practice Pan Calls.

Pilots may simulate emergency incidents, <u>but not the state of distress</u>, on 121.5 MHz, in order to enable them to gain experience of the service provided.

Before calling a D&D Cell, pilots should listen out on the emergency frequency, in order to ensure that no actual or practice incident is already in progress. Practice calls need not disrupt a planned flight or involve additional expense in fuel or time, since the pilot can request a 'diversion' to his intended destination or cancel the exercise when necessary.

Simulated emergency calls must be prefixed 'PRACTICE' and should be brief.

Practice Pan, Practice Pan, Practice Pan, London Centre, G-ABCD.

The Emergency Controller will then indicate whether or not he is prepared to accept the Practice Pan call. If he did accept, he would reply along the following lines:

G-CD, London Centre, Practice Pan acknowledged, Continue when ready.

The pilot would then pass details of the emergency he wished to simulate. The simulated message should contain relevant information that might help the D&D Cell, but should be as brief as possible.

Practice Pan, Practice Pan, Practice Pan, London Centre, G-CD, Cessna 152, Position Uncertain, Last known position Northampton, Time 25, Request fix and steer to nearest airfield, 2000 feet, QNH 998, Heading 090, Student Pilot, 1 POB.

G-CD, Roger, Trace indicating your position just West of Poddington, 8 nautical miles North of Cranfield, Nearest aerodrome is Cranfield, Steer 185.

Training Fix.

Pilots who do not wish to carry out a practice emergency, but require only to confirm their position, may request a 'Training Fix' on 121.5 MHz. The Training Fix is secondary in importance to actual emergency calls but takes precedence over practice emergency calls, in the event of simultaneous incidents. This type of call is initiated by words along the lines of:

London Centre, G-ABCD, Request Training Fix.

Seek the advice of your instructor, and consult CAP 413 for the latest information on RT phraseology to be used in a real or simulated emergency.

Once 121.5 MHz has been contacted and two-way communication established, pilots must not leave 121.5 MHz without telling the controller.

THE SPEECHLESS CODE

CAP 413 advises that, if an emergency message received by the military emergency controller is weak or distorted to the point of being unintelligible, the controller may ask the pilot to adopt the speechless code. To use the speechless code, the pilot presses on his transmit button a certain number of times, for short or long durations, in order to transmit carrier wave signals only. These signals, by convention, have the following meanings.

Number and Duration of Transmissions	Meaning
1 short	**'Yes'** or acknowledgement.
2 short	**'No'**.
3 short	**'Say again'** (to be used by the pilot when he has not fully heard the controller's transmission, or has not understood the transmission, or the transmission was an instruction and the pilot was unable to comply).
4 short ('H' in morse)	**'Request homing'** (to an airfield), or used for initial alerting. A civil pilot should only use the four short transmissions if he is aware, or suspects, before attempting to make initial contact with the Emergency Controller, that his own aircraft microphone is unserviceable. The Emergency Controller will then interrogate the pilot, using the call-sign 'Speechless Aircraft', if the identity of the aircraft is unknown.
1 long (2 secs)	**'Manoeuvre complete'** (e.g. steady on heading).
1 long, 2 short, 1 long	**'My aircraft has developed another emergency.'** ('X' in morse code.)

An aircraft SSR transponder can also be used, during times of communications difficulties, to acknowledge or respond to messages by the transmission of SSR code changes or squawking 'Ident' as requested by the controller.

MILITARY AERODROME TRAFFIC ZONES (MATZ) IN THE UNITED KINGDOM

Most military aerodromes in the United Kingdom which conduct regular flying operations have a Military Aerodrome Traffic Zone (MATZ) established around them, as well as a normal ATZ. The MATZ is of greater dimensions than the ATZ.

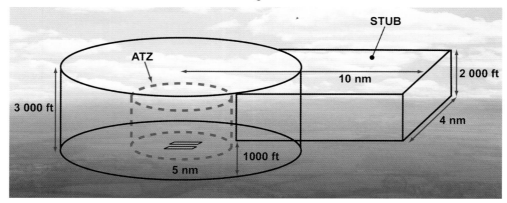

Fig 13.10 Dimensions of a Military Aerodrome Traffic Zone.

The Dimensions of Military Aerodrome Traffic Zones (MATZ).
A MATZ extends from the surface up to 3 000 feet above airfield level at a radius of 5 nm from the mid-point of the longest runway. *(See Figure 13.10).*

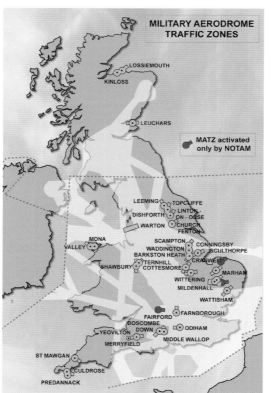

Fig 13.11 U.K. Military Air Traffic Zones.

The MATZ may have either one or two stubs projecting from it, to 10 nm from the mid-point of the runway, and having a width of 4 nm. The height of the stub(s) is from 1 000 feet AAL to 3000 feet AAL. A stub is an extension of the MATZ in the direction from which instrument approaches are made.

Sometimes, one or two neighbouring MATZs are amalgamated to form a Combined MATZ (CMATZ), with one of the aerodromes being designated as the controlling authority of the CMATZ.

The Locations of Military Aerodrome Traffic Zones (MATZ).
The locations of MATZs are depicted in *Figure 13.11*.

Operating Hours.
Operating hours for MATZs can be found in the ENR section of the AIP (unlike for the ATZ, where the operating hours are found in the AD section of the AIP). However, the nature of military operations is such that a MATZ may be required to be operational outside the notified hours.

Operating in and Penetration of a MATZ.

Although permission is not required from the MATZ controller to penetrate the wider MATZ (permission <u>is</u> required to enter the ATZ), a pilot would be foolish to enter a MATZ without contacting the MATZ controller.

When intending to enter or penetrate a MATZ, the pilot should make contact with the MATZ controller, either at a range of 15 nautical miles from the MATZ boundary, or at 5 minutes flying time from the MATZ boundary, whichever is the earlier.

The following general observations apply to the operation of civilian aircraft within a MATZ:

Fig 13.12 The Benson MATZ, as depicted on a 1:500 000 Aeronautical Chart, showing the ATZ at the centre of the MATZ.

Request a MATZ crossing 15 nautical miles or 5 mins from boundary, whichever is the sooner.

• Pilots must comply with any instructions issued by the MATZ controller and maintain a continuous listening watch on the MATZ frequency.

• Pilots should advise the MATZ controller when clear of the MATZ.

• QFE is the usual altimeter subscale setting used within a MATZ.

• Within a Combined MATZ, a "Clutch QFE" will be passed to aircraft. Clutch QFE is the QFE of the aerodrome within the MATZ whose elevation is highest.

• Maintaining terrain clearance is the responsibility of the pilot.

Pilots requiring a MATZ penetration service must establish two-way communication on the appropriate frequency with the aerodrome controlling the MATZ when 15 miles or 5 minutes flying time from the boundary, whichever is sooner.

When asked by the controller to "Pass your message", you should pass the following information:

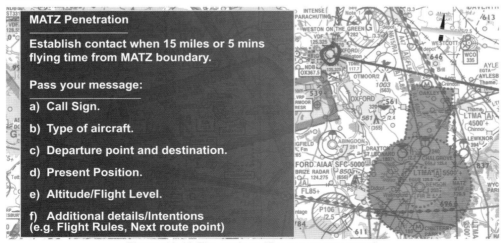

MATZ Penetration

Establish contact when 15 miles or 5 mins flying time from MATZ boundary.

Pass your message:

a) **Call Sign.**

b) **Type of aircraft.**

c) **Departure point and destination.**

d) **Present Position.**

e) **Altitude/Flight Level.**

f) **Additional details/Intentions (e.g. Flight Rules, Next route point)**

Figure 13.13 The reply to "Pass your message".

While the controller will make every effort to ensure safe separation from other aircraft, there may be civilian aircraft flying in the MATZ which are not known to the controller. Therefore, pilots must keep a careful lookout at all times.

Melsham Approach, G-ABCD, Request MATZ penetration.

G-ABCD, Melsham Approach, Pass your message.

G-ABCD, Cessna 172, from Netherbury to Wayford, 15 miles East of Melsham, Altitude 2500 feet, Southwold 1005, VFR, Estimate Melsham 52.

G-CD, Cross MATZ at 1500 feet on Melsham QFE 997 millibars, Report entering and leaving the MATZ.

Cross MATZ at 1500 ft on Melsham QFE 997 millibars, Wilco, G-CD.

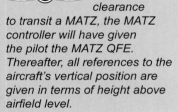

If a pilot has received a clearance to transit a MATZ, the MATZ controller will have given the pilot the MATZ QFE. Thereafter, all references to the aircraft's vertical position are given in terms of height above airfield level.

Notice that the MATZ controller passes the pilot the MATZ QFE, not a QNH. Consequently, all references to the aircraft's vertical position are references to height above airfield level.

LOWER AIRSPACE RADAR SERVICE (LARS).

The Lower Airspace Radar Service (LARS) was introduced in 1979 as a funding scheme to reimburse Air Navigation Service Providers for the provision of the radar service element of Air Traffic Services Outside Controlled Airspace (ATSOCAS).

All traffic flying IFR in controlled airspace will generally be in receipt of a radar service. In the United Kingdom, aircraft flying VFR in uncontrolled airspace may also be able to receive a surveillance radar service when in receipt of a Traffic or Deconfliction Service as part of the UK FIS, although provision of a service is at the controller's discretion, depending on primary workload. LARS forms an integral part in offering ATSOCAS.

A LARS is available from 29 participating Air Traffic Control Units, 15 of which are military and 14 of which are civilian.

Participating aerodromes are depicted in *Figure 13.14*. Aerodromes offering a LARS are listed in the En-Route Section of the United Kingdom Aeronautical Information Publication (UK AIP).

Significant Features of LARS.

- **LARS** is available **outside controlled airspace** up to and including **FL 95,** within the limits of radar/radio cover.

- **LARS** is provided within approximately **30 nms** of each participating aerodrome.

- **LARS** is normally available Mondays to Fridays between 0800 & 1700 hrs, in summer, and 0700 & 1600 hrs, in winter, although sometimes the service will be available outside these hours.

- While receiving a **LARS**, the pilot-in-command remains responsible for maintaining terrain clearance.

- The controller providing a **LARS** will not be aware of all aircraft which are operating in the airspace in which the aircraft <u>receiving</u> the **LARS** is flying. Therefore, a sharp lookout should be maintained at all times by pilots receiving a **LARS**.

When the LARS controller and the pilot requesting a LARS have established contact, and the LARS has been confirmed, the pilot should:

- Maintain a listening watch on the allocated frequency.

- Follow advice issued by the controller or, if unable to do so, inform the controller.

- Advise the controller when the service is no longer required.

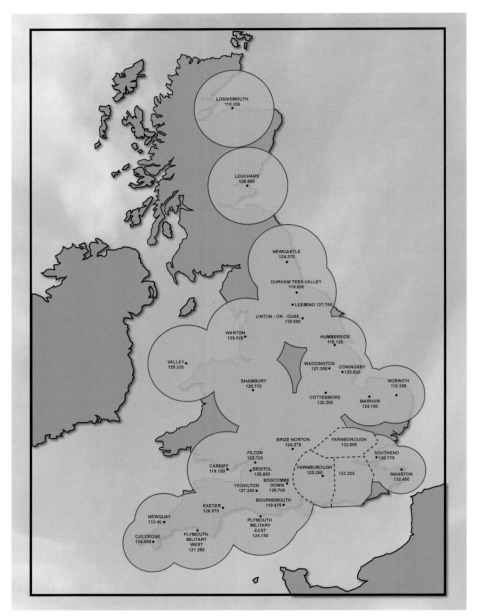

Fig 13.14 Air Traffic Service Units participating in the LARS.

AIR TRAFFIC SERVICES OUTSIDE CONTROLLED AIRSPACE

As stated in Chapter 6, the UK Flight Information Service (FIS) is a suite of services which includes Air Traffic Units and Air Traffic Control Centres. These provide a Flight Information and Alerting Service in uncontrolled airspace within the UK FIR.

The four distinct Flight Information Services are as follows:

1. Basic Service
2. Traffic Service
3. Deconfliction Service
4. Procedural Service

For a more in -depth explanation, see page 83.

It is the pilot's responsibility to determine the service required for his particular flight, and controllers will make all reasonable endeavours to provide the requested service.

HOW DO I ASK FOR A PARTICULAR SERVICE?

Steerton Approach, G-ABCD, Request *Basic/Traffic/Deconfliction/ Procedural Service.

Unless you are qualified to fly in IMC, you should accept a Traffic, Deconfliction or Procedural Service only in conditions where compliance with the radar controller's advice will permit your flight to continue in VMC.

G-ABCD, Steerton Approach, Pass your message.

G-ABCD, Cessna 172, From Notwood to Welcoombe, 5 miles North West of Steerton, Altitude 2500 feet, Southwold 1008, VFR.

A Basic Service does not give a pilot any advice or headings to fly in order to avoid conflicting traffic.

G-CD, No Known Traffic, *Basic/Traffic/Deconfliction/Procedural Service.

***Basic/Traffic/Deconfliction/Procedural Service, G-CD.**

*The pilot requests the service he requires, this is read back by the Air Traffic Unit, the pilot confirms that he understands that he is receiving a particular service, by repeating this in his acknowledgement message.

CHAPTER 14
VFR FLIGHT SCENARIO
IN THE UNITED KINGDOM

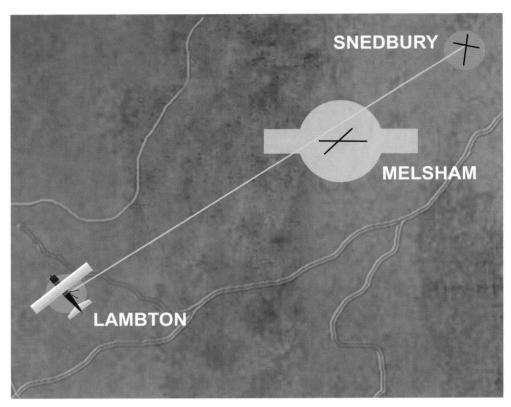

Figure 14.1 The VFR route from Lambton to Snedbury.

Station	Frequency
Lambton Ground	119.8
Lambton Tower	128.150
Lambton Approach	132.125
Metropole Information	125.750
Melsham Radar	120.7
Snedbury Information	120.475

Figure 14.2 VHF Communication frequencies required for the route.

VFR FLIGHT SCENARIO.

The following imaginary scenario depicts an aircraft on a **VFR** cross-country flight from **Lambton** to **Snedbury**. The scenario is typical of a **VFR** flight in the **United Kingdom**, outside regulated airspace. The scenario is included here to illustrate some of the points that have been made in this chapter about **VFR** flying in the **United Kingdom**.

The scenario begins with the aircraft on the ground at **Lambton**, a busy civil airfield with a full air traffic control service. The **RT dialogue** starts at the point where the pilot is ready to start the engine. **Lambton** does not have an **ATIS**.

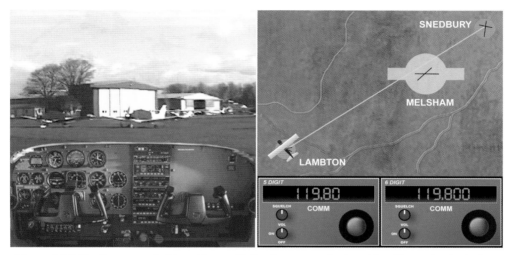

Figure 14.3 On the ground at Lambton, with the frequency for Lambton Ground selected on the radio.

Lambton Ground, G-ABCD, Radio check, 119.8.

G-ABCD, Lambton Ground, Readability 5.

Lambton Ground, G-ABCD, Cessna 172, At the flying club parking area, VFR from Lambton to Snedbury, Request departure information.

G-CD, Departure Runway 26, Surface wind 300 degrees, 6 knots, *QNH 1010, Temperature +6, Dew point +3.

As this flight scenario takes place in UK air space - atmospheric pressure is reported in MILLIBARS, unless it is greater than 1000, when the unit will be omitted from transmissions entirely.

Runway 26, QNH 1012, G-CD.

G-CD, Negative, QNH 1010.

QNH 1010, G-CD.

Some time later.

G-CD, Request taxi instructions.

G-CD, Taxi to Holding Point Delta One, Runway 26.

Taxi to Holding Point Delta One, Runway 26, G-CD.

The pilot is now at the holding point for Runway 26, with power checks and pre-take-off checks completed.

G-CD, Holding Point Delta One, Runway 26, Ready for Departure.

G-CD, Contact Tower, 128.150.

Tower, 128.150, G-CD.

Lambton Tower, G-ABCD, Ready for departure, Request right turn after take-off.

G-CD Hold position, Right turn approved, After departure climb not above altitude 1500ft until reaching the zone boundary, QNH 1010.

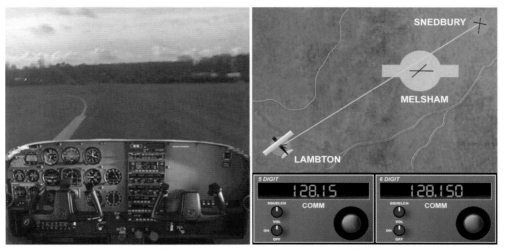

Figure 14.4 On the Tower Frequency, Ready for Departure.

Right turn approved, Not above 1500ft until zone boundary, QNH 1010, G-CD.

G-CD, Line up, Runway 26.

Lining up, Runway 26, G-CD.

G-CD, 300 degrees, 8 knots, Cleared for take-off.

Cleared for take-off, G-CD.

At some airfields, a pilot may be instructed to change frequency after take off, while, at others, local procedures may dictate when the pilot changes frequency. In this example, the pilot is instructed to change to Lambton Approach soon after take-off, even though he has not reached the control zone boundary. Note also that the approach controller instructs the pilot to report when certain conditions are met. For example, he tells the pilot to report reaching 1500 feet. It is important that the pilot should report promptly when reaching that altitude, because the controller may be waiting for this confirmation before issuing instructions to another aircraft.

G-CD, Contact Lambton Approach, 132.125.

Lambton Approach, 132.125, G-CD.

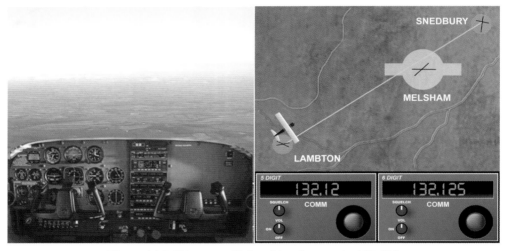

Figure 14.5 Airborne, with Lambton Approach, 132.125.

Lambton Approach, G-ABCD, Airborne from Runway 26, Turning right, Heading 040, Climbing to 1500ft, QNH 1010, En-route Snedbury.

G-CD, Roger, Report reaching 1500ft.

Wilco, G-CD.

G-CD, Maintaining 1500ft.

G-CD, Report at the zone boundary.

Wilco, G-CD.

G-CD, Zone boundary, Request Regional Pressure Setting.

G-CD, Roger, Southwold* 1008, Report leaving the frequency.

Southwold 1008, Wilco G-CD.

G-CD, Changing to Metropole Information, 125.750.**

G-CD, Roger, 125.750.

Metropole Information, G-ABCD, Request Basic Service.

*N.B.   Southwold is the fictional name of the altimeter setting region. Southwold 1008 is the regional pressure setting of 1008 millibars.

**N.B.   Metropole Information is the call-sign of the Basic Service provided by the fictitious Metropole Flight Information Region, in which the scenario unfolds.

G-ABCD, Metropole Information, Pass your message.

Metropole Information, G-ABCD, Cessna 172, From Lambton to Snedbury, 5 miles North East of Lambton, Climbing to altitude 2500 feet, Southwold 1008, VFR, Estimate Melsham 45.

G-CD, Roger, Basic Service.

Basic Service, G-CD.

When the pilot is within **15 miles**, or **5 minutes flying time**, of the **Melsham Military Aerodrome Traffic Zone (MATZ)** he informs Metropole Information that he is changing frequency.

Metropole Information, G-CD changing to Melsham Radar 120.7.

G-CD, Roger.

Figure 14.6 Approaching Melsham, with 120.7 MHz selected, the frequency of Melsham Radar.

Melsham Radar, G-ABCD, Request Traffic Information Service and MATZ penetration.

G-ABCD, Roger, Melsham Radar, Pass your message.

G-ABCD, Cessna 172, From Lambton to Snedbury, 15 miles South West of Melsham, 2500ft, Southwold 1008, VFR, Estimate Melsham 45, Request Traffic Information Service and MATZ Penetration.

G-CD, Roger, Traffic Information Service, Squawk 6512.

6512, G-CD.

G-CD, Identified 15 miles South West of Melsham, Set Melsham QFE 999 Millibars.

Note: Military units use **QFE** in the circuit and for **MATZ** penetration by civilian aircraft.

Melsham QFE 999 millibars set, G-CD.

G-CD, MATZ Penetration approved, Descend, Report level at height 1500 feet.

MATZ Penetration approved, Report level at height 1500ft, G-CD.

G-CD, Level at 1500ft.

 G-CD, Roger, Maintain.

 Wilco, G-CD.

Note that the **Melsham controller**, who is following the pilot's progress on radar, tells him when he is entering the **MATZ**. However, the pilot must be aware that when controllers are very busy they might ask pilots to call them when pilots are entering the zone.

 G-CD, You are entering MATZ, Runway-in-use 27, Right hand, Report overhead.

 Roger, G-CD.

 G-CD, Overhead, 1500 feet.

 G-CD, Report leaving the zone on track, Maintain 1500 feet.

 Wilco, G-CD.

 G-CD, Zone boundary, Heading 040.

G-CD, Roger.

As the pilot reaches the MATZ boundary and continues en-route to Snedbury, he remains with Melsham Radar from whom he is still receiving a Traffic Service.

In a Traffic Service, information about other traffic is passed to aircraft, but no advice is given on avoiding action to be taken. The pilot of the aircraft receiving the Traffic Service remains responsible for his own separation. A Traffic Service is available to all aircraft, whether IFR or VFR, and in any meteorological conditions.

While receiving a Traffic Service, the pilot can expect to receive frequent messages from the radar controller concerning traffic in the pilot's vicinity. If the pilot sees the traffic, he should report visual with the traffic. If he does not see it immediately, he can nevertheless acknowledge receipt of the radar controller's message with the words "Roger", followed by his call-sign. A typical RT exchange that you might experience while receiving a Traffic Service would be as follows.

G-CD, Traffic 12 o'clock, 6 miles, Crossing left to right, Indicating 400 feet above you and descending.

Roger, G-CD.

G-CD, Traffic, Left, 11 o'clock, 4 miles, Reciprocal heading, No height information.

Visual, G-CD.

G-CD, Squawk 7000, Freecall Snedbury on 120.475.

Squawk 7000, 120.475, G-CD.

Because Melsham Radar has asked you to "Freecall Snedbury", the radar operator is probably indicating either that he is too busy to continue the Traffic Service, or that you are getting beyond his radar range. In any case, because you are not under air traffic control and you have been invited to "Freecall Snedbury", you are aware that you are under no compulsion to contact Snedbury immediately.

You, therefore, elect to carry out a Practice Pan on 121.5 MHz, simulating being unsure of your position.

Before carrying out the Practice Pan procedure, there are a number of points you should note:

a)   You may simulate an Urgency Situation with the Distress and Diversion Cell, on 121.5 MHz, in the United Kingdom, but <u>you may not simulate the state of distress</u>.

b)   You may initiate the Practice Pan procedure but the D&D Cell to which you address your transmission will tell you whether or not you may continue. Listen out before transmitting to ensure another emergency is not in progress.

c)   You must think carefully about your Practice Pan call. Remember the purpose of a PRACTICE PAN is to give you a chance to transmit an emergency call and to give the controller practice in responding.

d)   You may terminate the Practice Pan any time you wish, but you must make it clear to the controller that is what you wish to do.

e)   Having once established two-way communication on 121.5 MHz, do not leave that frequency without informing the controller.

PRACTICE PAN, PRACTICE PAN, PRACTICE PAN, Metropole Centre, G-ABCD.

G-ABCD, Metropole Centre, Continue with PRACTICE PAN.

PRACTICE PAN, PRACTICE PAN, PRACTICE PAN, Metropole Centre, G-ABCD, Cessna 172, Unsure of position, Request fix and steer to Snedbury, Last known position 15 miles North of Melsham, 2500 feet, Heading 090, PPL, No instrument qualification, 2 POB, Endurance 2 hours.

G-CD, Roger, Trace is indicating your position 10 miles North East of Melsham, You are responsible for your own terrain separation, Your DF steer is 080, Range 20 miles.

Figure 14.7 Practice Pan on 121.5

080 degrees, 20 miles, G-ABCD.

G-CD, Do you require any further assistance?

Negative, Cancel Practice Pan, Changing to Snedbury Information, 120.475, G-CD.

At about 10 miles from Snedbury, having ended the Practice Pan, you have selected the frequency for Snedbury Information and listen out on that frequency while continuing towards Snedbury.

Snedbury Information, G-ABCD, Request joining information.

G-ABCD, Snedbury Information, Pass your message.

G-ABCD, Cessna 172, from Lambton to Snedbury, 10 miles South West of Snedbury, 2500 feet, Southwold 1008, Estimate Snedbury 25.

Note that joining <u>instructions</u> are issued only where a full air traffic control service is provided. In this example, Snedbury provides an Aerodrome Flight Information Service (as is evident from its call-sign INFORMATION). The pilot, therefore, requests joining <u>information</u> and it is then up to him to position his aircraft accordingly to join the circuit, safely and expeditiously.

G-CD, Runway in use 02, Left hand, Snedbury QNH 1010, Three aircraft in the circuit, Report downwind.

Runway 02, Left hand, QNH 1010, Wilco, G-CD.

Some minutes later.

G-CD, Downwind, Runway 02.

G-CD, Roger, Report final.

Wilco, G-CD.

G-CD, final.

G-CD, Land at your discretion, Surface wind 015, 8 knots.

Landing, G-CD.

G-CD, Runway vacated.

G-CD, Roger, Taxi to Flying Club via Taxiway Bravo, Report crossing Runway 12.

Taxi to Flying Club via Taxiway Bravo, Wilco, G-CD.

Figure 14.8 At Snedbury, on final approach.

SCENARIO ENDS

QUESTIONS

Representative PPL - type questions to test your theoretical knowledge of Radiotelephony.

1.   When arriving at an airfield with an Aerodrome Flight Information Service, a pilot receives the following call

        "G-EFIM, Land at your discretion, Surface Wind 230/08"

        Which of the following pilot responses to this radio call is correct?"

        a.   "At my discretion, 230/08, G-EFIM."
        b.   "G-EFIM." or "Roger, G-EFIM." or "Landing, G-EFIM."
        c.   "Cleared to land, G-EFIM."
        d.   "Land at my discretion. G-IM."

        (See Chapter 13)

2.   In a distress call, immediately following the MAYDAY prefix, what information should an aircraft next transmit, if circumstances permit:

        a.   The call-sign of the station addressed.
        b.   The position of the aircraft.
        c.   Aircraft type.
        d.   The nature of the emergency.

        (See Chapter 9)

3.   What should be the full content of a Distress call?

        a.   Station Addressed, MAYDAY, MAYDAY, MAYDAY, Call-sign, Position, Intention of Person in command.
        b.   PAN PAN, PAN PAN, PAN PAN, Position, Heading, Nature of Emergency, Intention of Person in command, Pilot Qualification, Any Other Useful Information.
        c.   MAYDAY, MAYDAY, MAYDAY, Call-sign of Station Addressed, Type of Aircraft, Nature of Emergency, Intention of Person in command, Position, Level and Heading, Pilot Qualification (wherever possible), Any other useful information.
        d.   MAYDAY, MAYDAY, MAYDAY, Nature of Emergency, Intention of Person in command, Endurance.

        (See Chapter 9)

4.   What should be the content of an Urgency call?

    a.   Station Addressed, PAN PAN, PAN PAN, PAN PAN, Call-sign, Position, Pilot Qualification Intention of Person in command.
    b.   MAYDAY, MAYDAY, MAYDAY, Position, Heading, Nature of Emergency, Intention of Person in command, Any Other Useful Information.
    c.   PAN, PAN, PAN, Call-sign of Station Addressed, Position, Nature of Emergency, Intention of Person in command, Endurance.
    d.   PAN PAN, PAN PAN, PAN PAN, Call-sign of Station Addressed (time and circumstances permitting) , Type of Aircraft, Nature of Emergency, Intention of Person in command, Position, Level and Heading, Pilot Qualification (wherever possible), Any other useful information.

(See Chapter 9)

5.   In United Kingdom RT Phraseology, which of the following options is correct regarding the wording of radio messages relating an aircraft's climb or descent to a HEIGHT or ALTITUDE?

    a.   The message should avoid all use of the word "to".
    b.   The message should employ the word "to", followed immediately by the word HEIGHT or ALTITUDE.
    c.   The message should employ the word "to", followed by the QFE or QNH.
    d.   The message should employ the word "to", followed immediately by the word LEVEL.

(See Chapter 13)

6.   Which of the following options best describes the purpose of a Special VFR clearance?

    a.   It enables a pilot to fly in the Open FIR with weather minima which are lower than for VFR.
    b.   It enables a pilot flying VFR to cross an airway.
    c.   It permits a pilot flying VFR to operate at his discretion within Control Zone.
    d.   It enables a pilot flying VFR to fly in a Control Zone where normally an IFR clearance would be required.

(See Chapter 5)

7.   Under what circumstances would a conditional clearance be used to direct movements on an active runway?

    a.   When an aircraft not equipped with a radio is landing or taking off.
    b.   When air traffic movements are particularly dense, provided it is safe to do so.
    c.   When all aircraft and/or vehicles included in the clearance can be seen by the controller issuing, and the pilot receiving, the clearance, and provided that the clearance relates to a single movement.
    d.   When vehicles not equipped with radio require to cross the active runway.

    (See Chapter 4)

8.   Which of the options below gives a correct order and content for a Position Report?

    a.   Call-sign, Route, Position, Level, ETA next Position, Heading, Request.
    b.   Call-sign, Position, Time, Level or Altitude, Next Position with ETA.
    c.   Position, Level or Altitude, Time, ETA at Next Position, Call-sign.
    d.   Route, Position, Time, Level or Altitude, ETA at Next Position, Call-sign.

    (See Chapter 3)

9.   Within what limits of accuracy is a VDF bearing which is passed to a pilot over the RT, and identified as a Class B bearing?

    a.   + or – 5 degrees.
    b.   + or – 3 degrees.
    c.   + or – 10 degrees.
    d.   + or – more than 10 degrees.

    (See Chapter 13)

10.   When requesting a Special VFR clearance, in flight, what details must a pilot pass to ATC?

    a.   Call-sign, Altitude, Heading, ETA at entry point of Control Zone.
    b.   Call-sign, Type, Heading, ETA at entry point of Control Zone.
    c.   Type, Heading, ETA at entry point of Control Zone, Call-sign.
    d.   Call-sign, Type, Intentions, ETA at entry point of Control Zone.

    (See Chapter 5 and 13)

11. Emergency procedures may be practised using the Frequency 121.5 provided that:

    a. The permission of the appropriate Control Centre has been previously obtained by telephone.
    b. The permission of the ATSU with which the pilot is in contact has been previously obtained.
    c. The procedure practised does not include simulating a condition of Distress.
    d. The procedure practised does not include simulating either a condition of Distress or a condition of Urgency.

    (See Chapter 13)

12. What are the three categories of aeronautical communication service?

    a. Air, Land and Sea.
    b. Approach, Tower, Ground.
    c. IFR, VFR, SVFR.
    d. Air Ground Communication Service, UK Flight Information Service, Air Traffic Control.

    (See Chapter 4 and 13)

13. When transmitting an emergency message, a pilot is required to give his aircraft's position as:

    a. The present or last known position, together with altitude or level, and heading.
    b. A GPS position.
    c. A position relative to the nearest airfield or aerodrome.
    d. A DME range from the station being addressed.

    (See Chapter 9 and 13)

14. Having obtained a clearance to cross a Military Aerodrome Traffic Zone (MATZ), a pilot is requested to maintain 2,500 feet on the MATZ QFE. All references to the aircraft's vertical position should, from that point, be made in terms of its:

    a. Altitude.
    b. Height.
    c. Flight Level.
    d. Minimum Vertical Separation Distance.

    (See Chapter 13)

15. If the pilot of G-ABCD wishes to obtain a true bearing from a VDF station, the correct RTF call to make is:

    a. G-ABCD, Request QDR, G-ABCD.
    b. True Bearing, True Bearing, G-ABCD, Request True Bearing, G-ABCD.
    c. G-ABCD, Request QDM, G-ABCD.
    d. QDR, QDR, G-ABCD, Request QDR, G-ABCD.

    (See Chapter 13)

16. Which of the following is a correctly worded Conditional Clearance, using United Kingdom phraseology?

    a. Whiteknuckle 248, After the landing 737, Line up.
    b. Whiteknuckle 248, Line up after the landing 737.
    c. Oxbow 321, Report Final, One ahead.
    d. Cheapo 742, Cleared for take-off, Caution Wake turbulence.

    (See Chapters 13 and 4)

17. The pilot of G-GOOD is carrying out a standard, overhead join at an unattended airfield in the United Kingdom. Which of the following RT calls indicates that he is commencing his descent in accordance with the standard procedure?

    a. G-GOOD, Crosswind, Descending.
    b. G-GOOD, Overhead, Descending.
    c. G-GOOD, Deadside, Descending.
    d. G-GOOD, Right Base, Descending.

    (See Chapter 13)

18. When requesting a clearance to cross a Military Aerodrome Traffic Zone, a pilot should pass information to the military controller with the following content and in the following order:

    a. Call-sign, Heading, Route, Present Position, Intentions.
    b. Call-sign, Aircraft Type, Departure Point and Destination, Present Position, Altitude or Level, Additional Details or Intentions.
    c. Aircraft Type, Route, Present Position, Additional Details or Intentions, Call-sign
    d. Call-sign, Altitude, Position, Intentions.

    (See Chapter 13)

19.   A pilot receives the following message from ATC.

        "G-HOPE, After departure cleared to zone boundary via Route Bravo, Climb to Altitude 2 500 feet, QNH 1005, Squawk 6521."

        What type of clearance is this?

        a.   A Take-off Clearance.
        b.   A Conditional Clearance.
        c.   A Departure Clearance.
        d.   A Route Clearance.

        (See Chapter 2)

20.   What should be the most correct content and order of a pilot's reply to the ATC instruction, "Pass Your Message"?

        a.   Aircraft Call-sign, Aircraft Type, Departure Point and Destination, Present Position, Altitude or Level, Additional Details and Intention (e.g. Flight Rules, Next Point on Route.).
        b.   Aircraft Call-sign, Aircraft Type, Departure Point and Destination, Present Position, Heading, Altitude or Level, Additional Details and Intentions, Request.
        c.   Aircraft Call-sign, Aircraft Type, Position, Heading, Level, Request.
        d.   Aircraft Type, Route Information, Position, Heading, Level, Additional Details and Intentions, Aircraft Call-sign.

        (See Chapter 6 and 13)

21.   In his initial call to Stealthy Approach, what words should be transmitted by the pilot of aircraft G-KEEN, if, during a cross-country flight, he requires a Flight Information Service?

        a.   Stealthy Approach, Golf Kilo Echo Echo November.
        b.   Golf Kilo Echo Echo November, Stealthy Approach.
        c.   Stealthy Approach, Golf Kilo Echo Echo November, Request Flight Information Service.
        d.   Golf Kilo Echo Echo November, Stealthy Approach, Request Flight Information Service .

        (See Chapter 6)

22.   You discover in your pre-flight planning that the air traffic service at your destination airfield is provided by an Aerodrome Flight Information Service Officer (AFISO). What will be the allocated RT call-sign of the of the ground station?

        a.   Information.
        b.   Radio.
        c.   Tower.
        d.   Approach.

        (See Chapters 4 and 13)

23.   You discover in your pre-flight planning that the air traffic service at your destination airfield is provided by an Air-Ground Communications Service. What will be the allocated RT call-sign of the of the ground station?

    a.   Information.
    b.   Approach.
    c.   Tower.
    d.   Radio.

    (See Chapters 4 and 13)

24.   On entering United Kingdom Airspace from an adjacent region where you have not been required to squawk a transponder code, what transponder code should you select?

    a.   7000
    b.   7600
    c.   2000
    d.   You would contact the appropriate FIR to ask for a transponder code.

    (See Chapter 7)

25.   'SQUAWK IDENT' means:

    a.   select the SSR transponder code to 7000.
    b.   select the SSR transponder mode to 'ALT'.
    c.   say again your call-sign.
    d.   operate the SSR transponder 'Special Position Identification' feature.

    (See Chapter 7)

26.   The phrase "Squawk Charlie" means:

    a.   transponder.
    b.   select 'ALT' on the transponder.
    c.   confirm the transponder is selected ON.
    d.   select 7700 on the transponder.

    (See Chapter 7)

27.   From which aeronautical communications service would you obtain automated broadcasts on aerodrome and weather information?

    a.   RIS
    b.   FIS
    c.   ATIS
    d.   AGCS

    (See Chapter 4)

28.   The frequency used for the initial transmission of a MAYDAY call should be:

     a.   the distress frequency 121.5 MHz.
     b.   the frequency on which the pilot is currently receiving a service.
     c.   any international distress frequency.
     d.   the approach frequency of the nearest airfield.

(See Chapter 9)

29.   An altitude of 1500 feet is transmitted as:

     a.   FIFTEEN HUNDRED FEET.
     b.   WUN TOUSAND FIFE HUNDRED FEET.
     c.   WUN FIFE HUNDRED FEET.
     d.   WUN FIFE ZERO ZERO FEET.

(See Chapter 2)

30.   The correct pronunciation of the frequency 122.1 MHz when passed by RT is:

     a.   WUN TOO TOO POINT WUN.
     b.   WUN TOO TOO DAYSEEMAL WUN.
     c.   WUN TOO TOO DECIMAL WUN.
     d.   WUN TWENTY WUN DECIMAL WUN.

(See Chapter 2)

31.   The word 'ROGER' means:

     a.   that is correct.
     b.   message received and understood.
     c.   pass your message.
     d.   I have received all of your last transmission.

(See Chapter 3)

32.   Which of the following is correct?

     a.   Runway 18 is passed as "Runway Eighteen".
     b.   "With you" means that you are on frequency.
     c.   ROGER means I have received all of your last transmission.
     d.   WILCO means I have received and understood the message.

(See Chapter 3)

33.   What is the Q code for a true bearing from a station?

     a.   QDR
     b.   QNH
     c.   QTE
     d.   QFE

(See Chapter 2)

34. What is the Q code for a magnetic bearing from a station?

    a.   QGH
    b.   QDM
    c.   QNH
    d.   QDR

(See Chapter 2)

35. Your radio check is reported as 'Readability 3', your transmission is:

    a.   unreadable.
    b.   perfectly readable.
    c.   reading only half the time.
    d.   readable but with difficulty.

(See Chapter 2)

36. Pilots requiring a MATZ penetration service must establish 2-way communications with the aerodrome controlling the zone when:

    a.   10 miles or 15 mins flying time from the zone boundary, whichever is sooner.
    b.   15 miles or 10 mins flying time from the zone boundary, whichever is sooner.
    c.   15 miles or 5 mins flying time from the zone boundary, whichever is sooner.
    d.   10 miles or 5 mins flying time from the zone boundary, whichever is sooner.

(See Chapter 13)

37. Which of these statements is true?

    a.   If you are receiving a Danger Area Activity Information Service the unit providing the service can also give you clearance to cross the danger area.
    b.   VFR flights are allowed in Danger Areas only if aircraft are equipped with a transponder fitted with Mode Charlie.
    c.   VFR flights are not allowed in Danger Areas under any circumstances.
    d.   If you are receiving a Danger Area Activity Information Service the unit providing the service cannot also give you clearance to cross the danger area.

(See Chapter 13)

38.   A pilot may file a flight plan with an ATSU during flight. The frequency that would normally be used for this purpose is:

a.   the frequency of the FIR in which you are flying.
b.   the Radar frequency of the ATSU with which you are in contact.
c.   the Approach frequency of the ATSU with which you are in contact.
d.   the Tower frequency of the ATSU with which you are in contact.

(See Chapter 3)

39.   What RT call would you make when you are ready to take off is?

a.   Request departure.
b.   Ready for take off.
c.   Request take-off clearance.
d.   Ready for departure.

(See Chapter 4)

40.   In the United Kingdom, when operating in the vicinity of a busy aerodrome, which has a high concentration of visual circuit traffic, what transponder code may the controller ask the pilot to select?

a.   7700
b.   7010
c.   7600
d.   7000

(See Chapter 2)

41.   If you wish to request a service from an Air Traffic Services Unit:

a.   you must do so in your initial call.
b.   you must do so after you have established two way communications with the station.
c.   you must monitor the ground station frequency until you hear the ground station giving the service you require to another aircraft.
d.   as a private pilot you are not entitled to request a service.

(See Chapter 2)

42.   A pilot may abbreviate his call-sign only:

a.   after having established communication with an aeronautical ground station on the frequency in use.
b.   when he considers no confusion with another similar call-sign is likely to occur on the frequency in use.
c.   when communicating with the departure and destination airfields.
d.   if it has first been abbreviated by the aeronautical ground station on the frequency in use.

(See Chapter 2)

43. Which of the following lists are all ATC messages that must read back in full:

    a. level instructions, altimeter settings, surface wind, runway information.
    b. clearance to enter, land on, take off on, backtrack, cross or hold short of an active runway; speed instructions, SSR instructions.
    c. VDF information, frequency changes, type of radar service, serviceability of approach aid.
    d. ATC route clearances, runway clearances, actual weather reports.

    (See Chapters 2 and 13)

44. On hearing a Distress message a pilot must:

    a. acknowledge the message immediately and standby to relay further messages if required.
    b. maintain radio silence and monitor the frequency to ensure assistance is provided.
    c. change frequency because radio silence will be imposed on the frequency in use.
    d. take control of the situation and co-ordinate the efforts of all agencies in the rescue operation.

    (See Chapter 9)

45. URGENCY is defined as a condition:

    a. of being threatened by serious and or immediate danger and of requiring immediate assistance.
    b. concerning the safety of an aircraft or other vehicle or of some person on board or within sight and requiring immediate assistance.
    c. concerning the safety of an aircraft or other vehicle or of some person on board or within sight, but which does not require immediate assistance.
    d. requiring urgent assistance from ground stations.

    (See Chapter 9)

46. What are the two classified states of Emergency Message?

    a. Emergency and PAN PAN.
    b. Distress and Urgency.
    c. MAYDAY and PAN PAN.
    d. Emergency and Security.

    (See Chapter 9)

47.   If making a straight-in approach, the FINAL call should be made at about:

      a.   2 nm
      b.   4 nm
      c.   8 nm
      d.   25 nm

(See Chapter 4)

48.   A condition of being threatened by serious and/or imminent danger and of requiring immediate assistance describes what category of message?

      a.   Distress.
      b.   Flight Safety.
      c.   Urgency.
      d.   Emergency.

(See Chapter 9)

49.   'STANDBY' means:

      a.   wait and I will call you again.
      b.   select STANDBY on the SSR Transponder.
      c.   hold your present position.
      d.   continue on present heading and listen out.

(See Chapter 3)

50.   Which of the following messages has the highest priority?

      a.   CAUTION, WORK IN PROGRESS ON THE TAXIWAY.
      b.   REPORT FINAL NUMBER 1.
      c.   REQUEST QDM.
      d.   TAXY TO THE REFUELLING PUMPS.

(See Chapter 2)

51.   Which statement is correct?

      a.   A VHF Direction Finding message has priority over a flight safety message.
      b.   A meteorological message has priority over a flight safety message.
      c.   An urgency message is lower priority than a flight safety message.
      d.   A "windshear" warning has a higher priority than "cleared to take off".

(See Chapter 2)

52.   Altitude is defined as:

a.   the vertical distance of a level, a point or an object considered as a point, measured from mean sea level.
b.   the vertical distance of a level, a point or an object considered as a point, measured from another point.
c.   the vertical distance of a level, a point or an object considered as a point, measured from an aircraft.
d.   the vertical distance of a level, a point or an object considered as a point, measured from an airfield.

(See Chapter 2)

53.   Which transponder mode gives an altitude readout:

a.   Mode Alpha.
b.   Mode Bravo.
c.   Mode Charlie.
d.   Mode Delta.

(See Chapter 7)

54.   What are the 4 categories of Flight Information Service?

a   Basic, Radar Information, Radar Advisory, Procedural
b   Basic, Normal, Collision Avoidance, Procedural
c   Basic, Traffic, Deconfliction, Procedural
d   Basic, Normal, Deconfliction, Procedural

(See Chapter 13)

55.   What is the Q-code for a magnetic bearing to a VDF station?

a.   QGH
b,   QDM
c.   QDR
d.   QTE

(See Chapter 2)

56.   Frequency 121.725 MHz should be transmitted as:

a.   ONE TWO ONE POINT SEVEN TWO.
b.   WUN TOO WUN DAYSEEMAL SEVEN TOO FIFE.
c.   WUN TOO WUN POINT SEVEN TOO.
d.   ONE TWENTY ONE DECIMAL SEVEN TWENTY FIVE.

(See Chapter 2)

57.   Certain words may be omitted from transmissions provided no confusion will result. Which of the following underlined words must not be omitted?

    a.   SURFACE in relation to surface wind and direction.
    b.   FEET in relation to altitude or height.
    c.   DEGREES in relation to radar headings.
    d.   CLOUD in meteorological reports.

(See Chapter 3)

58.   Loss of communications is indicated by which transponder code?

    a.   7700
    b.   7600
    c.   7500
    d.   7400

(See Chapter 8)

59.   When transmitting a message preceded by the phrase "Transmitting blind due to receiver failure" the aircraft station shall also:

    a.   advise the time of its next intended transmission.
    b.   hold for 5 minutes at its present position.
    c.   proceed to the alternate airport.
    d.   enter the next en-route holding pattern.

(See Chapter 8)

60.   Radio test transmissions should take the following form:

    a.   station being called, aircraft identification, words "Readability check", frequency.
    b.   station being called, aircraft identification, words "radio check", frequency being used.
    c.   station being called, aircraft identification, words "How do you read?".
    d.   station being called, aircraft identification, frequency, words "Do you read?".

(See Chapter 2)

61.   The point to which an aircraft is granted ATC clearance is the:

    a.   limit point.
    b.   clearance limit.
    c.   no go point.
    d.   point of No Return.

(See Chapter 4)

62.   Taxy instructions issued by the controller will include a clearance limit which will normally be:

        a.   the threshold of the runway in use.
        b.   the entrance to the parking area.
        c.   the holding point of the runway in use.
        d.   the holding point of an intermediate runway.

        (See Chapter 4)

63.   Which of these statements is true?

        a.   When making an initial call from an aircraft to a ground station you must state the ground station name and suffix first and then your abbreviated call-sign.
        b.   When making an initial call from an aircraft to a ground station you must state the ground station name and suffix first and then your full call-sign.
        c.   When making an initial call from an aircraft to a ground station you must state your full call-sign first and then the ground station name and suffix.
        d.   When making an initial call from an aircraft to a ground station you must state your abbreviated call-sign first and then the ground station name and suffix.

        (See Chapter 2)

64.   What is the meaning of the UK term FREECALL when used by an ATSU to a pilot in flight?

        a.   Call (designator of unit/frequency), when you choose to do so.
        b.   Call (designator of unit/frequency), before contacting your destination airfield.
        c.   Call (designator of unit/frequency), passing what information you judge relevant to the safe continuation of your flight.
        d.   Call (designator of unit/frequency) and pass your full details on first contact.

        (See Chapter 13)

65.   If a pilot receives an instruction from ATC which he cannot carry out, he should use the phrase:

        a.   UNABLE.
        b.   NEGATIVE INSTRUCTION.
        c.   NO CAN DO.
        d.   CANCEL INSTRUCTION.

        (See Chapter 2)

Question	1	2	3	4	5	6	7	8	9	10	11	12
Answer	b	a	c	d	b	d	c	b	a	d	c	d

Question	13	14	15	16	17	18	19	20	21	22	23	24
Answer	a	b	b	a	c	b	d	a	c	a	d	c

Question	25	26	27	28	29	30	31	32	33	34	35	36
Answer	d	b	c	b	b	b	d	c	c	d	d	c

Question	37	38	39	40	41	42	43	44	45	46	47	48
Answer	d	a	d	b	a	d	b	b	c	b	b	a

Question	49	50	51	52	53	54	55	56	57	58	59	60
Answer	a	c	a	a	c	c	b	b	b	b	a	b

Question	61	62	63	64	65
Answer	b	c	b	d	a

JAR-FCL THEORETICAL KNOWLEDGE SYLLABUS

VFR COMMUNICATIONS

The table below contains the principal topical and subtopics from the current outline syllabus for the **JAR-FCL theoretical knowledge examination in VFR Radiotelephony Communications,** as published in **JAR-FCL 1.**

Syllabuses may be modified, so always check the latest examination documentation from your **national civil aviation authority**, or from **JAR-FCL/EASA.**

COMMUNICATIONS	
Radiotelephony and communications:	use of AIP and frequency selection; microphone technique; phonetic alphabet; station/aeroplane call-signs/abbreviations; transmission technique; use of standard words and phrases; listening out; required 'readback' instructions.
Departure procedures:	radio checks; taxi instructions; holding on ground; departure clearance.
En-route procedures:	frequency changing; position, altitude/flight level reporting; Flight Information Service; weather information; weather reporting; procedures to obtain bearings, headings, position; procedural phraseology; height/range coverage.
Arrival and traffic pattern procedures:	arrival clearance; calls and ATC instructions during the: circuit, approach and landing, vacating runway.
Communications failure:	Action to be taken (alternate frequency; serviceability check, including microphone and headphones); in-flight procedures according to type of airspace.
Distress and urgency procedures:	distress (Mayday), definition and when to use; frequencies to use; contents of Mayday message; urgency (Pan), definition and when to use; frequencies to use; relay of messages; maintenance of silence when distress/urgency calls heard; cancellation of distress/urgency.

The JAR-FCL/EASA theoretical knowledge examination in VFR Communications in the United Kingdom.
In the **United Kingdom Radiotelephony Manual, CAP 413,** the **United Kingdom Civil Aviation Authority (UK CAA)** states (CAP 413, 1 May 2006, Foreword, Page 1) that students preparing for **JAR-FCL/EASA** pilot examinations should note that the syllabus for the **VFR Communications** theoretical knowledge examination

is drawn directly from **ICAO Annex 10, Volume 2,** and from the **ICAO Manual of Radiotelephony, Document 9432-AN 925**, and not from **CAP 413**.

While this statement is authoritative, and holds good for students preparing the theoretical knowledge examinations for **Commercial Pilot Licences (CPL)** and **Airline Transport Pilot Licences (ATPL), United Kingdom-based candidates for the JAR-FCL PPL will, almost invariably, be required to sit a VFR Communications paper which contains questions on UK Radiotelephony (RT) practices.** This is because, for **UK-based PPL candidates**, the separate written examination paper for the **Flight Radiotelephony Operator's Licence (FRTOL)** - a solely **UK** licence - may be used for both the **FRTOL test** and for the **PPL theoretical knowledge examination in VFR Communications**.

Before taking the **RT Communications theoretical knowledge examination**, therefore, **UK-based PPL candidates** must learn both the **ICAO practices** <u>and</u> the **United Kingdom differences** thoroughly, and, during the examination, apply the **UK RT differences**, where appropriate.

The official source for **UK RT practice** is **CAP 413**. **CAP 413** may be purchased in book form, or accessed via the **UK CAA's website**.

CPL and **ATPL** students should note that they will be tested on **ICAO** practices only during their theoretical knowledge examinations. Always consult the official syllabus before presenting yourself for an examination.

The United Kingdom Flight Radiotelephony Operator's Licence.
RT communications between **United Kingdom Air Traffic Service Units** and **pilots** are expected to comply with the phraseology described in **CAP 413**.

All **United Kingdom-based candidates for pilot licences** will be required to take a written and practical test for the **United Kingdom Flight Radiotelephony Operator's Licence (UK FRTOL)** <u>in addition to</u> the theoretical knowledge RT examination. The **UK FRTOL** is a **UK national licence** issued under different legislation from **JAR-FCL/EASA pilot licences**.

The written test for the UK FRTOL contains questions on ICAO practices and United Kindom differences. Before taking the **UK FRTOL** test, candidates should learn both the **ICAO practices** and the **United Kingdom differences** thoroughly, and, during the test, apply the **UK differences**, where appropriate.

The practical **UK FRTOL** test consists of a written examination and a practical communications test with an authorised **RT** examiner. The practical test is carried out in an **RT** simulator. The candidate is briefed to "fly" a typical light aircraft route from one aerodrome to another, passing through a **Military Aerodrome Traffic Zone** and, possibly, at some stage, into or through a **Control Zone**. The candidate is required to make all the appropriate radio calls and frequency selections as if he were actually flying the route. The examiner performs the function of an **Air-Ground Communications Service Operator**, **Aerodrome Flight Information Service Officer**, or **Air Traffic Controller**.

Full details of the **FRTOL** are contained in the **UK CAA** publication **LASORS** (Licensing Administration Standardisation Operational Requirements Safety).

Index

5-Digit Display   7
6-Digit Display   7
8.33 kHz Frequency Spacing   5
25 kHz Spacing   3
121.5 MHz   118, 122, 163, 188

A

Abandon Take-off   62
Abbreviated Call Signs   20
Abbreviations   40
ACGS Radio Operator   167
Aerodrome Control   49
Aerodrome Flight Information Service (AFIS)   51, 165
Aerodrome Flight Information Service Officer (AFISO)   165
Aerodrome Terminal Information Service (ATIS)   74
Aerodrome Traffic Zone (ATZ)   51, 165
Aeronautical stations   18, 186
Aircraft Call-signs   19
Aircraft Ready for Departure   169
Air/Ground Communication Service   53, 164, 167
Air Traffic Control Centres (ACC)   84
Air Traffic Control Service   49
All Stations   120
Altitude   5, 17, 18, 29, 99, 179
Approach Control   73
Arriving VFR Traffic   73
Attenuation   128
Automatic Direction Finding (ADF)   3, 40
Automatic Terminal Information Service (ATIS)   55, 134
Avoiding Action   98, 197

B

Basic Flight Information Service   83, 84, 196

C

CAP 413   161
Categories of Aeronautical Communications Service   164
Categories of RT Messages   29
CAVOK   40
Circuit Traffic   101, 176
Classes of Bearing   186
Clearances and Readback Requirements   30
Closing   96
Communications Failure   109

Conditional Clearance	30, 60, 179
Conspicuity Code	99
Continuation of Established Communications	21
Controlled Airspace	49, 73, 89
Converging	96
Crossing a Runway	169
Crossing Left to Right/Right to Left	96

D

Danger Area	182
Danger Area Activity Information Service (DAAIS)	184
Danger Area Crossing Service (DACS)	182
Deconfliction Flight Information Service	84, 85, 86 196
Departing Aircraft	55, 78
Direction Finding	27
Direction Finding Messages	29
Direct Wave	130
Distress	29, 117, 119
Distress and Diversion (D&D) Cell	188

E

Emergency	117
Essential Aerodrome Information	166
Establishing Communication	20

F

Final Approach and Landing	67
Flight Information Service	
- *Basic Service*	84
- *Deconfliction Service*	85
- *Procedural Service*	86
- *Traffic Service*	85
Flight Plans	45
Flight Regularity Messages	29
Flight Safety Messages	29
Frequency Selection	8

G

General Operating Procedures	11, 163
Go Around	68
Ground-Reflected Wave	130

H

Horizon Ray	129
Hours of Service	163

I

ICAO Annex 10 Volume 2	161
ICAO Manual of Radiotelephony	18
ILS	40, 126
Imposition of Silence	120

L

Level Instructions	41
Listening Watch	88, 163, 193
Long Final	67
Lower Airspace Radar Service (LARS)	195

M

Mandatory Readback	178
MATZ Penetration	193
MAYDAY	118
Meteorology	129
Meteorological Messages	29
Military Aerodrome Traffic Zone (MATZ)	192
Millibars	6,41
Missed Approach	68
Mode Alpha	100
Mode Charlie	100
Mode Sierra	103

N

NDB	10, 126
Numbers	16

O

Overhead Join	74, 111, 178
Overtaking	96

P

Pan Pan	29, 118
PANS ATM, Document 4444	161
Pass Your Message	39, 181
Phonetic Alphabet	15
Practice Pan	190, 210

Procedural Flight Information Service   84, 86, 196
Propagation   125, 128

Q

Q Code   26
QDM   27, 187
QDR   27, 186
QFE   28, 40
QNH   29, 40
QTE   28, 188
QTE (UK)   186

R

Radar Phraseology   93, 102
Radar Services   93
Radio Frequencies   10, 126
Radiotelephony   3, 13, 161
Radio Test Procedures   25
Readability   26
Relaying an Urgency Message   121
Runway Vacated   70
Runway Visual Range (RVR)   18, 40,135

S

Safetycom   176
Secondary Surveillance Radar (SSR)
  - *Airborne Collision and Avoidance Systems (ACAS)*   103
  - *IDENT*   101
  - *SQUAWK*   101
Secondary Surveillance Radar (SSR)   99
Special VFR (SVFR)   185
Special VFR (SVFR) Flights   79
Speechless Code (UK)   191
Squawk   17, 102
Squelch Control   9
Standard Words and Phrases   37
Standby Frequency   8
States of Distress or Urgency   117
Straight-in Approach   67

T

Take-off Procedures   58
Taxi Instructions   56
Termination of Distress Traffic   120
Traffic Circuit   63
Traffic Flight Information Service   83, 85, 196
Traffic Information   96

Training Fix   190
Transit   76
Transit the ATZ   172
Transmission of Time   18
Transmitting Blind   110
Transponder   3, 100

U

UK Supplement (UK)   159, 199
Unattended Aerodromes   176
Urgency   29, 117

V

VDF-equipped aerodromes   189
Vehicles   62
VFR Flight (UK)   201
VHF and HF Frequencies   10
VHF Direction Finding (VDF)   10, 126, 186
VOLMET   133, 136

W

Weather   131
Weather Information   133